JERSEY WEATHER AND TIDES

Cover: Surf breaking over sea wall at St. Ouen's (photo courtesy Jersey Tourism)
Portrait of the author in front of St. John's Parish Church (photo courtesy Peter Trenchard)

Snow lies on the ground in Jersey at 9 am on three days a year on average.
(Photo Jersey Evening Post)

JERSEY WEATHER and TIDES

Peter Manton

Fellow of the Royal Meteorological Society

SEAFLOWER BOOKS

Published in 1995 by SEAFLOWER BOOKS
16¹ᐟ² New St. John's Road, St. Helier, Jersey

Seaflower Books is an imprint of
EX LIBRIS PRESS
1 The Shambles, Bradford on Avon
Wiltshire, BA 15 1JS

Typeset in 11 point Contemporary Brush

Design and typesetting by Ex Libris Press
Cover printed by Shires Press, Trowbridge, Wiltshire
Printed and bound in Britain by
Cromwell Press Ltd., Broughton Gifford, Wiltshire

© Peter Manton

ISBN 0 948578 75 0

To my wife

Give me your hand
And I will surely climb
To splendid heights
Conquering mountains as the eagles do.

Give me your love
And I will trade with Time
For added years
In which to give it back to you

That which hath been is now; and that which is to be hath
already been;... and there is nothing new under the sun.
Book of Ecclesiastes.

CONTENTS

Mont Orgueil Castle (Mount Pride) under snow. It was built 1204, the main bastion of defence against an enemy. It was betrayed into the hands of the French in 1461 and the Island was occupied until 1468.

PREFACE

It was in 1931 when I was eleven that I decided to go in for the Weatherman's Badge in the Scouts. I was required to make a rain gauge and record the weather, noting the direction and strength of the wind, and the cloud formation. I got hooked.

When the airport was being built in 1937, I applied for a job in the meteorological office but they had never heard of such a job, nor, indeed, of such a place. In the event I helped Mr. C. G. F. Bewsey who gave station reports to the pilots with the permission of Commander Phillips, the commandant who was followed by Charles Roche. Neither of us was paid to begin with but Geoffrey Bewsey, who played cricket for Jersey, was put in charge of the office and I was his assistant.

Before the airport was built aircraft landed on the beach between West Park and First Tower. The managing director of a Hertfordshire bus company was sick on the sea journey and the humiliation caused him to start Jersey Airways with 8-seater de Havilland 84s, and later DH 86s with fourteen seats. Passengers booked in at half a bus without seats. The other half was the Customs shed. The police cleared people away when aircraft operated but the wheels of one aircraft coming in to land passed either side of a boy's head. The first aircraft was from Jersey to Portsmouth on 18 December, 1933. The London airport was Heston, but the main airport was Croydon in the earliest days.

After the war I worked at the Met. Office for thirteen years before taking Holy Orders. The work consisted of observing the weather and plotting the weather maps from a code. Guernsey was station No. 894 and Jersey 895. The lights of the airport had been sent to Southampton for safety before the Occupation but were bombed and destroyed there, so the airport was open only during daylight hours. We worked throughout. They were long days in summer.

When lighting was restored we were on shifts. Aircraft on Fridays and Saturdays came in until 1 a.m. in summer, but years of campaigning against noise caused the airport to close earlier. Nevertheless it was necessary to rise at 2.30 a.m. and go to work in order to do the 3 a.m. observation for the pilot of the newspaper plane. Few know what goes on behind the scenes before the morning paper comes through the letterbox at breakfast time. Now the observations go on at half-hourly intervals while the airport is open.

Jersey Airways became the Channel Islands Airways and was the largest and most successful of all domestic airlines. A pilot named Jack Keene-Miller became its managing director. After Winston Churchill was dismissed in 1945 the Queen sent for him and said, "I am going to give you the Order of the Garter". Churchill replied, "I cannot accept it ma'am. I have just been given the Order of the Boot". Clem Attlee became Prime Minister and started nationalising everything including all domestic airlines. Channel Islands Airways was registered locally and refused to join British European Airways as ordered. We governed ourselves and would have none of it. Britain said in that case our aircraft would not be allowed to land in England. Jersey caved in to this blackmail and B.E.A. Dakotas appeared on the runway. Rapides were the other key aircraft. It must be said that Channel Islands pilots and staff were absorbed by B.E.A.. B.E.A. started on 1 April, 1947, after the Order in Council had extended the new Act of the Bailiwicks of Jersey and Guernsey. Jack Keene-Miller became B.E.A.'s Channel Islands Area Manager without moving office.

Pilots were pretty well all ex-R.A.F. personnel. Jack Keene-Miller was one who was ultimately shot down after D-Day but landed in a small field and was captured and put on a prison train. He escaped and got back to our lines. There was a very high level of discipline among pilots. They wandered into the Met. Office and were given forecasts which were made at the London Headquarters of the Meteorological Office, later Dunstable and Bracknell. The station reports were obtained by the Radio Department of the airport, now Telecommunications. They took it all down by morse. It was called GFA for British stations and HXX for French stations. Later came teleprinters and computers.

The Jersey Meteorological Office is now staffed by highly qualified forecasters and assistants and is fully equipped with the latest inventions. The Weather Radar at La Moye, which looks like a golf ball, cost a million pounds and it enables forecasters to see rain and storms seventy miles away. The forecasts are done on an independent basis and are not forecasts compiled on the mainland. One purpose of this book is to stress the variableness of weather – Jersey and Guernsey can be very different – and forecasters on the mainland can only speak of the Channel Islands.

Jersey is especially fortunate in having St. Louis Observatory because records go back for more than a hundred years. Very few places on the mainland have an unchanged site of such age. The value is in the long-term averages and records of storms going back into the last century. The station opened on 1 January, 1894, and on 5 January it recorded a minimum air temperature of −10.3°C or 13.8°F. The record still stands in 1995. Jersey is indeed a key station and ranks among the best and most respected in the British Isles. It also brings out an annual report which is exceedingly comprehensive and which should be made available to the public and to schools.

In the earliest days of radio – Daventry 5XX – there was a shipping forecast at 10.30 a.m. after the station opened with the Daily Service at 10.15 a.m. It was read at dictation speed because nothing could be recorded then. There was a weather forecast at 6 p.m. and 9 p.m. for today and tomorrow plus an outlook. Today we gets forecasts for up to six days. They are

remarkably accurate basically but timing can go wrong. Rain can be forecast for Wimbledon six days ahead but the public dismisses it as hopeless if the rain falls the night before or the night after, with play as usual by day.

It is doubtful if accurate forecasts will ever go beyond a week but there could be a general weather type forecast for a month or more. In early January, 1963, when there was high pressure from Greenland through Iceland to Scandinavia and Siberia, forecasters in Norway and Sweden said that bitter cold weather would go on until March. It did. In the brilliant summers of 1989 and 1990, with barometric pressure uniformly high and steady, forecasters were going in for a good summer.

In the 1930's there was a station called Weather London which did nothing but give actual station reports, forecasts and upper air readings. Croydon was a key station and Jersey an auxiliary station. All very useful to pilots, farmers and others. The station was kicked out because somebody wanted the wavelength, but it was a mine of information not so easily available today.

The proper title of this book should be *Jersey Weather and Tides and Other Things*. This is because the weather affects us all every day of our lives wherever we may be and governs the quality of crops, holidays, business and recreation. It also profoundly affects travel by sea and air and has an impact upon health. It is for these reasons that the book is written and it is my hope that at least some schools will consider using it so that the coming generation will have more knowledge of our being granted the exalted title of 'Sunny Jersey' plus the distinction of having one of the greatest tidal ranges in the world.

Temperatures are given in Fahrenheit and Centigrade because half the population has never understood Centigrade and don't want to know anyway. The younger generation has never been taught Fahrenheit. What is interesting is that in summer a temperature of 82°F has a far greater impact than

28°C. And there is also the thrilling 100°F or 38°C which is always just out of reach here. In the winter, however, a temperature of 0°C does register even with the Fahrenheit fanatic. So when we talk about −2 or −6 the intensity of frost does having meaning. Rainfall is also given in inches and millimetres.

Thanks are due for help and advice generously given by: The Royal Meteorological Society; La Société Jersiaise; Roger Thébault, Principal Meteorological Officer, States Airport; Syd Rogers, forecaster, St. Louis Observatory; Frank Le Blancq, forecaster; Jennifer Holley, née Grundy, forecaster; Harry Graham, forecaster; Roy Bullen, Harbourmaster; H. W. Carrel, *Jersey Evening Post*; M. B. Kavanagh; Christopher Manton; Sylvianne Manton; Captain Bernard Picot; Peter Bisson; Dr. John Renouf; Roy McLoughlin; Ian James, Managing Director, Jersey New Waterworks Company; John Hobbs, sometime Managing Director, Jersey New Waterworks Company; Rodney Clarke, sometime Managing Director, Jersey New Waterworks Company and Michael Le Caudey.

Quotes have been made from the *The Great Western at Weymouth* (David and Charles, 1971) by kind permission of the publishers. Also from *Mail Ships of the Channel Islands* by Richard Mayne (Picton Publishing, 1971). Weather Lore quotes are largely from *Weather Lore* by Richard Inwards, sometime President of the Royal Meteorological Society (1990) and are reproduced with the kind permission of the Royal Meteorological Society. *Quaternary Changes in Sea Level and Climate*: Seminar Report 1, Global and Climatic Change, Irish Sea Forum, by Professor R. T. R. Wingfield (University of Liverpool Press, Liverpool) is quoted with the author's kind permission.

PETER MANTON
Gorey Village, JERSEY
September 1995

Reservoir in Waterworks Valley, September 1976 – see **Great Drought of 1975 - 76**. *(Photo courtesy Reg Quérée)*

A BRIEF HISTORY OF JERSEY

IF YOU TAKE a group of young people to the north coast of Jersey on a very clear day it is possible to see cars coming down the hill at Carteret as well as the beaches and houses. Everyone will ask the same question, why are we English and not French?

In 913 AD, by the Treaty of St Clair-sur-Epte, Charles the Simple, King of France, ceded the Duchy of Normandy to Rollo, the Chief at that time of the Vikings, who for the previous hundred years had invaded the coasts and rivers of France.

In 1066, William, Duke of Normandy, fifth in direct descent from Rollo, invaded England. He was crowned King William I of England on Christmas Day 1066, the first crowning ever to take place in Westminster Abbey. As the Duke of Normandy was our Duke, we claim that we had won England with him. Indeed, some Jerseymen are said to have taken part in the Battle of Hastings.

In 1204, King John of England and Duke of Normandy lost the continental portion of the Duchy of Normandy, and the Island had to decide whether to go back to France or remain loyal to King John. They chose King John, and thus the French coast suddenly became an enemy coast. It led to the building of Gorey Castle which, from 1461, became known as Mont Orgueil Castle (Mount Pride).

So that is why we are under the Crown and not France. But what is hardly ever taught is why we chose King John and not France. Some time after Helier brought Chritianity to Jersey in 558AD, monks settled on what is now Elizabeth Castle and built an abbey. They brought Christianity, welfare, medical care and education to the people of the Island. They were greatly loved. But, in 1185, nineteen years before people had to decide between England and France, the Abbot of Cherbourg downgraded the Abbot of Jersey to Prior, and took away many of the monks to the fury of the people. So when they were asked in 1204 whether they would go back to France the answer was 'never.' Jersey became part of the Crown of England and the oldest dominion. In 1270 King Edward I granted the seal of the Bailiwick.

In 1481 a traitor betrayed Mont Orgueil Castle, the bastion of our defence, into the hands of the French. They occupied the Island until 1468 when Sir Richard Harliston laid siege to the castle and regained it after nine months of fighting by land and sea.

The French occupied the western part of the Island — St Mary and St Ouen. La Rue de la Frontière in St Mary was the frontier between the French and Jersey people. However, modern historians believe that the Island was fully occupied but that the western parishes were the most hostile.

The Seigneur of St. Ouen was the leader of the resistance. One day when he was fishing in St. Ouen's Pond — La Mare au Seigneur — the French furtively crept along the beach towards him. He sprang to the saddle and drove his horse furiously. The beast made an enormous jump over a sunken lane 18 feet deep and 22 feet across which no enemy horse could equal. He made it to the manor but the horse dropped dead under him. It was buried in the grounds with full military honours.

King Charles 1 was executed at sunrise on 30 January 1649 and his son, Prince Charles, fled to Jersey where he found sanctuary. Be lived for a time at Elizabeth Castle. He worshipped at the Parish Church of St. Helier, inspected the Militia — the oldest unit in the British Army — and visited Mont Orgueil Castle. He was proclaimed King on 17 February 1649 in the Market Place, and again in 1660 at the Restoration before he was proclaimed King in London. The people of Jersey were the first to acknowledge him as King Charles II. In 1663 the King gave the Royal Mace to the Island, ordering that it should be carried forever before the Bailiffs in perpetual remembrance of their fidelity. He confirmed that the Island was excused all taxes made by Parliament, hence 'NO VAT' in the shops is proclaimed to this day. Jersey's freedom and independence were underlined by the event, and is acknowledged by the Royal Family in these days also.

On 6 January 1781, the depth of winter, French troops landed at La Rocque – Platte Rocque – led by Jersey pilots who were traitors. The weather had delayed the event several times. The huge force under Baron de Rullecourt marched to St. Helier using St Clement's church as a barracks. A young girl in Colomberie called out from an upper storey window, "Ou donc est la garde?" ("Where are the guards?") They replied, "Elle dorme, ma cherie." ("They are sleeping, my dear.")

Major Moses Corbet, Lieutenant Governor of Jersey, was caught at Government House, then in Grosvenor Street, and forced to sign a surrender order by de Rullecourt. He was taken to Major Francis Peirson and told him to surrender as he had been surprised and caught out. Peirson replied that he had not been surprised and was not surrendering. Meanwhile a French officer was trying to persuade Major Mulcaster to surrender, telling him that there were 10,000 Frenchmen on the way. "All the better," replied Mulcaster, "there will be more to kill." So the battle commenced in the Market Place, later known as the Royal Square. Both Peirson and Rullecourt were killed. The French then surrendered.

The danger from France was not over because of the rise of Napoleon. A great number of Martello towers were built, and the foundations of Fort Regent were laid by General Don in 1806. St. Catherine's Breakwater was started in 1847. The signal stations at this time were of crucial importance because there was no other form of communication. Service in the Militia – Royal from 1831, the 50th anniversary of the Battle of Jersey – was compulsory from the earliest days until 1928 when it became voluntary. The Militia dates from 1337.

Once Jersey became an island it had an identity which became world-wide. It is incredible that people on this tiny island found the Jersey cow which is famous throughout the world. It is because of the sea that we are able to stop imports of other cows. It is because the weather gives us a degree or two of warmth more than south-west England that enables the Jersey Royal potatoes to come on the British market before any others. It is because of the sea that King Charles found sanctuary which was denied him on the mainland; it is because of the sea that we can govern ourselves.

The first occupation of Jersey was from 1461 to 1468; the second was from 1940 to 1945. In each case the enemy was stuck because we are an island. No food, military stores or ammunition reached Mont Orgueil Castle in 1468. Nor could there be any reinforcements. The German forces were isolated after D-Day, 6 June 1944. In the end the Germans were starving as were the people of the Island. The Germans could not withdraw nor could there be any reinforcements.

Bombings were governed by the weather. Islanders who escaped could only do so in calm weather. Rough seas caused many deaths through drowning, while fog was a great help. There were stories of noble heroism and grievous suffering. The Island has now passed out of darkness into light and it is the ardent hope of us all that we shall have many centuries of peace in the future as were granted to us in the past.

I quote some words from Deuteronomy: 'For the Lord thy God bringeth thee into a good land, a land of brooks of water, of fountains and depths that spring out of valleys and hills. A land wherein thou shalt eat bread without scarceness; thou shalt not lack anything in it, a land which the Lord thy God careth for; the eyes of the Lord are always upon it, from the beginning of the Year even unto the end of the Year.'

11

A summer gale smashed the railings of the bridge dividing the paddling pool from the main pool at Havre des Pas. A raft broke adrift and battered it on 6 August 1961.
(Photo Jersey Evening Post)

ST. LOUIS OBSERVATORY

ONE OF THE MOST familiar sights in Jersey before the war were the French boys, as we called them. They were young Jesuits who were stationed at Maison St. Louis, and were studying theology in order to be ordained priests. About 3,000 passed through Jersey, and they were never any trouble. They were here because of hostility by the French Government towards schools of religious orders.

According to Forecaster F. W. Le Blancq, the property known as 'Le Clos de la Fregonnière' belonging to the Ingouville family came on the market in 1838; the States opposed the sale, but in 1893 Father Marc-Antoine Dechevrens bought it with the approval of his superiors, and set up an observatory to continue his meteorological studies.

Maison St. Louis itself was built as an hotel: the Imperial Hotel, before the Jesuits arrived — and it returned to the status of an hotel when they left: the Hotel de France. One bar used to be the chapel of the Jesuits. The Observatory was built by Mr. S. Cuzner of Great Union Road for £531. However Father Dechevrens had a Belgian Company build a tower 50 metres (150 feet) high to record the wind at a level above the surface. That cost £1,260.

This tower looked like the Eiffel Tower and it was the dominant landmark of Jersey. It was seen by ships coming from France or Guernsey. Valuable recordings of various aspects of meteorology were made at the top of the tower, and it was tragic that the cost of maintenance was too great to keep it going; it was brought down on 29 February, 1929. It was an enormous tower, and there was much speculation in the Island as to what would happen if it did not fall where it was supposed to. But it did.

The observations started on 1 January, 1894. On 5 January a record low minimum temperature of −10°C (14°F) was noted. It still stands for the station a hundred years later. On 7 February, 1895, the lowest February temperature of −9.5° was recorded. That still stands. The brilliant Father Dechevrens who was the author of 125 papers left the Island in 1909 due to ill heath. He died in 1923.

There was a gap in the observations from 1921-1924 inclusive. This was unfortunate as 1921 was the driest year with 16 inches of rain. Father Christian Burdo took over on 1 January, 1925. He was another brilliant scientist who came to the Island in 1901. Meteorology and archaeology were his specialist subjects, and he took part in digs at La Pinnacle, St. Ouen and La Cotte, St. Brelade. Although he retired as Director in 1934, he continued with his work in the Island, and died in 1961.

In May 1934 one of his pupils, Father Charles Rey, took over as Director and stayed on after the Jesuits left the Island until 1979 — a lifetime of work for Jersey. He died in 1981. He borrowed a Mainka seismograph from the Faculté des Sciences de Strasbourg for two years, but it is still there. Jersey became a very important seismograph station, the only one in the Channel Islands. There were not many in England either in those days. We used to hear on the wireless, 'an earthquake was recorded at Selfridges, London ... ' In Jersey, Maison St. Louis Observatory became famous for its seismograph, while Selfridges's found that the seismograph was better than advertising in the papers. It was a lot of work for Père Rey who had to use smoked paper. He once remarked that he could train a pupil to work the seismograph in a few weeks, but it would take seven years to learn how to interpret what the seismograph recorded and work out where the earthquake occurred. It was remarked earlier that the coldest day in 100 years happened a few days after the observatory opened in 1891. Père Rey recorded an earthquake a few minutes after setting up the seismograph in 1936. His meteorological readings were always published in the Annual Bulletin of La Société Jersiaise.

Père Rey continued his observations throughout the Occupation. He had the remarkable distinction of being appointed The Official Timekeeper of Jersey. The Germans therefore allowed him to keep a wireless set. He gave the correct time to people having public clocks because nobody was supposed to have a wireless.

When Père Rey spoke to the Germans, he often swung his large pocket watch which hung on the end of a chain. The Germans didn't know that it contained a crystal set! He made many crystal sets for people as, indeed, he made most of the instruments in the observatory.

The B.B.C. announcer Alvar Lidell came to open a fête at St. John's Manor about 1972. He was deeply moved, almost to tears, when a number of people came to him and showed him matchboxes containing crystal sets, most of which were made by Père Rey. "We heard you right through the Occupation, sir", they said.

One day a German came to the Observatory and told Père Rey that they were going to knock down the Observatory and build garages for the military. The Director begged him not to, and pleaded for his beloved Observatory the whole morning. "When the Officer left," he said, "I went outside and was physically sick on the ground."

In May 1945 he had a fit when he saw the same officer striding towards him. The officer stopped, saluted, and said, "I surrender to a gentleman" — and handed him his sword. He was indeed a gentleman, and he was a brilliant scientist. He was made an Honorary Life Member of La Société Jersiaise, a private Society, but one regrets that the States appear to have no way of honouring somebody who has done so much for the Island over a remarkably long period. Père Burdo comes into the same category.

Few people realise just how valuable a station which has run for over a hundred years is in the field of meteorology. There are not many stations in Britain which have run for so long on the same site. Maison St. Louis cost the States nothing and its dedicated Directors were unpaid. It is disgraceful that the States of the day did not help paint the mast in 1929, and it had to come down. In 1955 the States refused to buy the Observatory for a paltry sum of £5,000 when Père Rey was likely to leave with the Jesuits. He stayed, and the States bought the property and land for £7,500 — the best bargain the States have ever made. Since that time the Observatory has been run by Mr. Syd Rogers, a forecaster from the Met. Office. It became Jersey's official Health Resort Station under Père Rey, and continues to this day. It is of priceless value to tourism and farmers, and it has always been recognised by the British Meteorological Office as a key station. In the early days the readings were sent by telegram to London. The station is the most southerly in the British Isles.

MAISON ST. LOUIS RECORDS

Coldest night	5 January 1894	−10.3°C (13.5°F)
Hottest day	3 August 1990	35.4°C (95.7°F)
Coldest month	February 1895	−1.0°C (30°F)
Warmest month	July 1983	Mean temperature 21.1°C (69.9°F)
Coldest year	1963	Mean temperature 10.2°C (50.36°F)
Warmest year	1989	Mean temperature 12.9°C (55.22°F)
Earliest air frost	6 November 1980	
Latest air frost	12 April 1986	
Earliest ground frost	11 September 1972	
Latest ground frost	18 June 1918	
Wettest day	24 August 1931	95.7 millimetres (3.76 inches)
Wettest month	November 1910	266.4 millimetres (10.48 inches)
Wettest year	1960	1107.06 millimetres (43.606 inches)
Driest months	June 1976 and June 1925	0.2 millimetres (0.008 inches)
Driest year	1921	426 millimetres (16.77 inches)
Longest drought	21 July to 28 August 1976	39 days
Longest spell with rainfall	11 November to 12 December 1960	32 days
Highest 5-minute wind speed	13 November 1940	62 knots

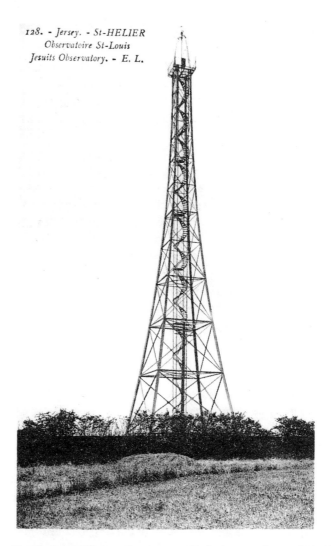

128. - Jersey. - St-HELIER
Observatoire St-Louis
Jesuits Observatory. - E. L.

The St. Louis Observatory meteorological tower. It was felled in 1929 because of the cost of maintenance. It was a notable landmark.

THE BAROMETER

NO MATTER WHERE we live in the world, we have to endure the weather from the moment of birth until death. The weather, or climate, governs the food that we grow, the location of rivers, forests and various animals and birds. It also affects health.

In attempting to explain weather, we can consider two basic factors. The first is that warm air, being lighter than cold, rises and is able to contain more moisture than cold. So tropical rainfall can be huge, while precipitation in polar regions is small by comparison. There is some truth in the expression, 'it is too cold for snow.' Some of the blizzards at the Poles are blown snow, not fresh snow. Usually more snow falls when the temperature is near freezing point.

The second is that air tries to equalise pressure differences in the same way as water seeks its own level. However, air is not able to flow directly from high to low pressure. It circulates anti-clockwise, slightly inwards towards a low, and clockwise round a high, in the northern hemisphere. This is caused by the rotation of the earth, and is known as the Coriolis Force. Buys Ballot's Law says, 'if you stand with your back to the wind in the northern hemisphere the barometer will be lower on your left than on your right. Stand with your back to the wind in the southern hemisphere, the barometer will be lower on your right than on your left.'

A barometer measures the weight of air pressure upon you whether you are at sea level or at the top of a mountain. If you have a well 40 feet deep, and you extract the air in the pipe leading down to the well, the weight of the air upon the water in the well will force the water up the airless pipe to a height of 30 feet. After that a deep-well pump is necessary to extract water to a higher level. The weight varies from day to day —

sometimes 29 or 28 feet, and perhaps 31 feet. As a barometer of 40 feet is impractical, we use mercury which has a higher specific gravity. So 30 feet becomes 30 inches. The empty part of a tube of a mercury barometer is a vacuum, so the air pressing on the mercury cannot support a column of mercury more than about 30 inches high. The weight varies from day to day, and is noted every 30 minutes in every key meteorological station. It is recorded in millibars. A reading of 30 inches is 1015.9 millibars, and 29.5 inches is 1000 millibars.

What we have to learn is that an altimeter is also a barometer, or, if you like, a barometer is also an altimeter. If you take the wall barometer in the car and read it at the top of Bouley Bay Hill, or Bonne Nuit Hill, and drive to the bottom, the reading will have risen by about half an inch because of the effect of the weight of air of the extra 400 feet acting on it. Ten millibars, or one third of an inch, is equivalent to about 300 feet at sea level. It is worth taking a barometer on a motoring holiday to the mountains. You can calculate roughly the height of the mountain.

An aircraft will be sitting on the ground at Jersey Airport, and the altimeter will show zero feet. If the pressure falls 10 millibars, it will show the aircraft to be flying at 300 feet even though it is still on the ground. The pilot will obviously set the altimeter to show that it is on the ground before moving off. However, if he is flying to Glasgow where the pressure might be 20 millibars lower because of a depression near the Hebrides, the aircraft would be hitting the chimney pots when the pilot thought he was at 600 feet. But we must not be alarmist. The pilot is told what pressure to expect in Glasgow, and the controller tells him what it is during the flight, so the pilot sets his altimeter to read zero feet when he touches down. The utmost care is taken by the observer reading the barometer, and the controller.

All pressure readings are reduced to mean sea level before being sent to the Met. Office at Bracknell. So, if the Jersey reading at sea level is 1020 millibars, the pilots approaching Jersey will be given 1010 millibars because the Airport is nearly 300 feet above sea level – 277 feet to be exact. In aviation the pilots 'Q' code is used and the sea level reading is known as the QFF, and the airport reading is known as the QFE. So when a pilot receives the QFE he sets his altimeter so that it reads zero feet when he touches down.

Only sea level readings are plotted on a map, and the lines joining places having the same pressure are called isobars. The isobars show the location of depressions and anti-cyclones, and from them the direction and speed of the wind can be calculated. The closer the lines or isobars are together, the stronger the wind.

As mentioned, the pressure falls ten millibars, or a third of an inch, every thousand feet. Very high ground affects athletes, causes water to boil at a lower temperature, and makes one light-headed. It is almost necessary to wear oxygen masks to climb Mount Everest at 29,000 feet, although it has been done without. Early aircraft had great difficulty in flying at such a height because of the low pressure and temperature.

The highest and lowest pressures are normally in January, or a month either side, and therefore gales tend to be at their fiercest because of the tightness of the 'pressure gradient' i.e. there are a large number of isobars between high and low pressure. The contrast is least in June, and the month either side, so the winds are at their lightest.

Forecaster F. W. Le Blancq notes that the highest pressure recorded at Maison St. Louis Observatory was 1051.7 millibars on 29 January, 1905. That is 31.05 inches. The lowest, recorded at the Airport was 953.8 millibars on 25 February, 1989. That is 28.17 inches.

Within mainland Britain the highest was 1054.7 millibars in January, 1902, at Nairn, Scotland, and the lowest 925.5 in January, 1884, at Ochtertyre, Scotland.

The world highest reading is 1083 millibars on 31 December, 1968, at Agata U.S.S.R. and is just about 32 inches which is not marked on a normal wall barometer. The lowest world reading is 870 millibars recorded on 12 October, 1979, at the centre of Typhoon 'Tip' at 16°N 138°E. That is 25.7 inches, and is not remotely possible to record on a wall barometer. The needle would turn half a circle anti-clockwise.

Any reading of 1044 millibars or above in Jersey, (30.8 inches) is very high, and anything lower than 970 millibars (28.64) is very low. Frank Le Blancq has researched the occasions when these figures have been exceeded:

HIGHEST PRESSURE RECORDED EACH MONTH IN JERSEY, U.K. AND EIRE

Month	Jersey	Date	UK & Eire	Date	Place
JAN	1051.7	1905	1054.7	1902	ABERDEEN
FEB	1047.9	1882	1051.1	1902	NAIRN
MAR	1047.7	1990	1047.9	1990	ISLES OF SCILLY
APR	1040.5	1938	1044.5	1938	ESKDALE-MUIR
MAY	1039.3	1920	1042.2	1943	DUBLIN
JUN	1036.3	1959	1043.1	1959	CLONES
JUL	1034.0	1969	1038.3	1911	NORTH SHIELDS
AUG	1035.7	1949	1036.7	1949	PEMBROKE
SEP	1037.0	1947	1038.6	1906	KEW
OCT	1039.1	1930	1045.6	1956	DYCE
NOV	1041.9	1930	1044.5	1956	BENBULA
DEC	1045.7	1905	1051.9	1926	WICK

Month	Jersey	Date	UK & Eire	Date	Place
JAN	970.4	1919	925.5	1884	OCHTER-TYRE
FEB	953.8	1989	942.3	1951	CORK
MAR	967.4	1914	946.2	1876	WICK
APR	976.4	1899	952.9	1948	MALIN HEAD
MAY	987.1	1885	968.0	1943	SEALAND
JUN	988.8	1965	976.8	1944	WICK
JUL	987.6	1894	976.0	1922	TYNE-MOUTH
AUG	983.7	1917	967.8	1957	SULE SKERRY
SEP	977.2	1952	987.1	1953	CLARE-MORRIS
OCT	964.4	1987	946.8	1891	CAWDOR CASTLE
NOV	962.0	1916	939.7	1877	MONACH L/HOUSE
DEC	958.7	1896	927.2	1886	BELFAST

With a few exceptions, the highest and lowest pressures occurred in January or a month either side, and the weaker highs and lows in June and the month either side.

Above 1044 Millibars		Below 970 Millibars	
1051.7 (31.05 ins)	29 Jan 1905	953.8 (28.17 ins)	25 Feb 1989
1049.4	18 Jan 1882	958.7	04 Dec 1896
1047.9	20 Feb 1882	962.0	18 Nov 1916
1047.8	15 Jan 1902	964.3	18 Nov 1880
1047.7	23 Feb 1883	964.3	04 Feb 1951
1047.7	03 Mar 1990	964.4	16 Oct 1987
1047.0	07 Feb 1964	964.7	08 Dec 1954
1046.9 (28.50 ins)	15 Feb 1934	965.4	29 Nov 1965
1046.5	30 Jan 1896	965.6	18 Nov 1880
1046.0	30 Jan 1989	966.7	20 Dec 1925
1045.7	30 Dec 1974	967.2	20 Nov 1926
1045.1 (30.86 ins)	12 Dec 1905	967.4	20 Mar 1914
1044.9	16 Feb 1959	968.3	04 Dec 1876
1044.7	20 Jan 1983	968.4	13 Nov 1940
1044.2	25 Feb 1918	968.4	02 Dec 1976
1044.1	26 Jan 1932	968.5	13 Mar 1951
		969.1	12 Nov 1915
		969.4	09 Oct 1964
		969.5	22 Feb 1914
		969.6	01 Feb 1930
		969.8 (28.63 ins)	28 Mar 1888

The pressure of 968.4 on 13 November, 1940, during the Occupation, marked the most severe gale recorded at Maison St. Louis Observatory according to the late Père Rey. The 969.4 on 9 February, 1964 marked the very severe gale which sank a yacht, and only one young lady survived. The 964.4 on 16 October was associated with the near hurricane which in 1987 destroyed thousands of trees in the Island, and millions of trees on the mainland.

WATER SUPPLY AND RAINFALL

WHEN HELIER LIVED on the Hermitage rock off what is now Elizabeth Castle and brought Christianity to Jersey, the population was said to be 2,000. Later census figures are as follows:

1821	28,600
1841	47,544
1851	57,020
1871	55,627
1891	54,518
1911	51,898
1931	50,462
1951	57,310
1971	69,329
1991	84,842

These figures are astonishing. The increase in the population in 1851 to 57,020 was caused by the persecution of religious bodies by the French Government. Note that the population more than doubled from 1821 when there were only 28,600 people. The population has never been below 50,000 since 1851 except for 1921 when there were 49,701.

Today there is uproar over the increased population, but it has only gone up from 57,310 since 1951 (when it was the same as 1851) to what is now 86,000.

The percentage rise from 1851 to 1995 is 50.8 but the percentage rise from 1821 to 1851 was 100.1. That is nothing compared to the mainland when populations have trebled at least in the same period, and in some cases have gone up ten times.

The incredible thing is that there were no housing estates in 1851. Virtually no schools – Victoria College opened in 1852;

no waterworks, no drains, no electricity, no radio and no telephone or telegraph.

In 1861 the population of St. Helier was 29,528. There was no piped water, and very few sewers. The Grand Douet was an open brook consisting of two streams which met north of St. Helier and which flowed by what is now La Coie Hall Hotel, formerly the Jersey Modern School. This was a valuable washing place in addition to other things.

Although the Jersey Waterworks Company was founded in June, 1863, and had a registered office in Westminster, the thing which really got a piped water supply going was an outbreak of cholera of epidemic proportions in 1867. A well was sunk in St. Lawrence Valley, now known as Waterworks Valley, and a 12-inch main was laid to St. Helier 'for breweries, hotels, houses and gardens,' but the two wells were unable to meet the demand, and the company went bankrupt after two dry summers in 1874. So there was no piped water for the next eight years.

Part of the Engineer's Report at the time, kindly supplied by Mr. John Hobbs, is reproduced on the following page.

In spite of all this, there was not a real water supply for the Town or the Island until after the First World War.

The mean average demand of 12-15 gallons per person per day was maintained both here and on the mainland until after the Second World War. It has to be remembered that many houses did not have bathrooms.

After the war a major upgrading of the Island's drainage system was led by George Gothard who forecast that the demand was likely to be nearer 17 gallons and that he should legislate for 22 gallons. He was right.

To the Honorary Committee of the Jersey Waterworks

Gentlemen,

After careful examination of the whole of the watersheds of this Island, and most of the principal streams, it is my deliberate opinion that it will be best to arrange, to collect, and take the water at, or near, the mouth of the streams entering St. Aubin's Bay, in accordance with the Act of the States, which sanctions the concession under which this Company is working.

The water supply of the Island is derived from the rainfall, part of which runs off into the sea, part is absorbed by vegetation, part is evaporated, and the remainder is absorbed by the ground, a portion of which emerges by natural springs, the greater part finding its exit on the southern side in St. Aubin's Bay. This would seem an ample supply.

This quantity would give nearly three million gallons per day, equal to 75 gallons per head per day for 40,000 people, this being one fourth in excess of the population to be at present provided for.

The only water obtained in St. Helier at present, is from wells in the Town, and gives but little of its rainfall to be used for domestic purposes. The stream passing Town Mills is only fit for flushing the sewers, and is only used for that purpose.

The water in each of these three streams (particularly that of Millbrook Valley) is very good and soft, and rises from springs at their source and in the Valleys. The source of Millbrook, in the St. Lawrence Valley, is near Brook House, belonging to Mr. George Dorey, formerly the property of St. Sydney James Nicolle, and is in the Parish of St. John. There are other springs about half a mile below the first springs, adjacent to the main road, and near Mr. David Romeril's house. This stream receives the waters from contributing springs all the way to the mouth. The source of the spring to St. John's Valley is from good springs on Mr. Le Brun's Farm, known as St. Germain, in the parish of St. John. These springs have never been known to give less water than at present. (August and September 1869).

The St. Lawrence Valley has a Watershed of nearly 1,500 acres, which, with a rainfall of 28 inches will give 900 million gallons per year. The requirement for 35,000 people, at 15 gallons per head, is 525,000 gallons only, leaving an amount of excess of 275,000 daily. In many towns in England, the consumption of water does not exceed 12 gallons per head per day, in others, where the consumption is unusually great, on account of the large hotels, breweries etc. and watering the streets and roads several times a day, the quantity of water consumed, on the average, by each person, does not exceed 14 gallons per day, whilst St. Helier will be provided with 15 gallons per day.

In many towns supplied with water, the consumption does not exceed the following:- Brighton 14 gallons; Ramsgate, Ipswich, Ryde, Tunbridge Wells Deal, Grantham, Reigate and others, 10-12 gallons per day for each person.

I propose that every house, factory, and other places to be supplied shall have either a cistern or water-meter so as to ensure as little waste as possible. It is cleanliness, ventilation, and drainage, and the use of perfectly pure drinking water that populations ought to look mainly for safety against nuisances and infections. It is generally known that, while the population of St. Helier has greatly increased, there has not been a commensurate increase in its supply of pure water.

The Grand Douet, the water of which was available for household purposes, is now so contaminated by the opening of privies and drainage of stables, pig-sties etc. into it, and the admixture of foul soap-suds, has to be little better than an open sewer when it reaches the Town. Water thus tainted has been found to occasion Typhoid Fever, Dysentery, Diarrhoea, and Choleric disorder. The present outbreak of Cholera (February, 1867) amongst ourselves, has served to illustrate the fact. It commenced in a locality where the water was known to be impure. A large proportion of the subsequent cases have occurred in a circumscribed situation, where the well water was so impregnated with sewerage, as to become offensive when drawn for a few hours. It is, therefore most important to secure a due supply of pure water from country districts, before it has become corrupted by injurious admixture.

In addressing this representation to you, the members of the Medical Board, wish to keep strictly within its own proper limits, leaving to others the advocacy of the measure, on such grounds as the general improvement in the value of property, the lessening of poor rates, the due provision for the extinguishing of fire, and last, but not least, the common claims of humanity.

The foregoing was signed by John Fixott, M.D., President, John Le Crosier, M.D., Martin M. Bull M.R.C.S.L. and Thomas Kitchener M.D.

William Henry Le Feuvre, Engineer,
September 28th, 1869

Recently the demand here has risen sharply to 30 gallons per person per day, and touches 40 gallons in a summer heatwave peak. There has been a huge house-building programme down the years — all with bathrooms.

On 23 May, 1881, a local business man, Mr. Cleveland Masterman, convened a meeting of twenty influential people, and the Jersey New Waterworks was formed. We might remember that the New Waterworks Company is now 115 years old. It was registered in the Royal Court on 11 February, 1882.

The Company started off building Millbrook Dam, and in 1914 a second reservoir was constructed in Waterworks Valley at Dannemarche. But what really got things going was the driest year of the century, 1921, with 16.77 inches of rain. In fact, the three consecutive driest years since records began were 1920, 1921 and 1922 with an annual average of 26.27 inches.

In 1932 Handois Reservoir above Waterworks Valley was built, and in 1934 a steam abstraction plant at La Hague in St. Peter's Valley was added to improve the reservoir yield. Chlorination was introduced at the Millbrook slow sand filters in 1921, but was converted to chloramine in 1934 and that has been the main sterilisation process ever since.

It is not always obvious to everyone that the higher a reservoir is located the better, because water moves by gravity. The houses at sea level get the greatest pressure. Nevertheless, pumping is done on a large scale because many homes are on high ground. In the old days there was a water tower — one of many — at First Tower. It was actually on the Martello Tower.

It is tedious to describe all the work of the Jersey New Waterworks Company, but it should be said that they kept ahead of demand by a whisker, and by brilliant planning and foresight. They built the Grands Vaux Reservoir in 1953, and Val de la Mare in 1960. But the boldest decision was taken in 1965 to build a desalination plant on land at La Moye owned by the Le Quesne family. The family gave way for the good of the people. It was, in fact, crucial to the well-being of the Island because the drought of 1975 and 1976 brought us within an ace of running out of water at the height of the visitor season. The La Rosière plant provided 209 million gallons of water in 1976, and only a deluge of rain starting in September and giving 20 inches by 31 December, saved the day. Has anyone ever thought what it would be like for a full hotel to have no water coming from taps, and no water to flush lavatories? Plans were made to bring in tankers.

The next decision to be made in 1976 was to flood Queen's Valley. Incredibly there was mass opposition from the people and members of the States. The lesson of 1976 vanished from the mind. It took thirteen years to get started amid demonstrations and many votes in the States, some just in favour, but ultimately a large majority.

The building of Queen's Valley Reservoir was the greatest engineering feat in the history of the Island. It virtually doubled the Island water storage capacity. It had to be doubly strong because of the risk of earthquakes or tremors. A burst reservoir makes world news, and is a major disaster, and it has to be safe even in violent rain storms which fill it to capacity. A very great amount of thought and care has gone into it, and it is safe, and a great credit to the Company. The planting of trees and shrubs, the provision of paths and seats, have combined to make it a very pleasant walk, and there are many thousands of visitors. Even the most hostile opponents of the scheme have been converted. The water supply of the Island is safe well into the next century. It was opened in 1991.

LA ROSIERE DISTILLED SEA WATER PLANT

Year	Millions of Gallons	% of Total Water Supplies
1976	209	20
1984	52	4
1988	68	5
1989	193	15

Total consumption of oil: 43 tons per day.

RESERVOIR CAPACITY AND COST

	Year	Capacity (Million Galls)	Cost
Millbrook	1895	8	£6,767
Dannemarche	1909	24	£14,125
Handois	1931	45	£41,828
Grands Vaux	1948	50	£195,000
Val de la Mare	1961	207	£600,000
Desalination Plant	1970		£1,200,000
Queen's Valley	1991	262	£17,000,000

As was mentioned earlier, the 57,000 people who lived in Jersey 150 years ago used well water and water from streams. The water table survived because people lived on a pitcher of water each day.

If the 84,000 people today, not counting visitors, had no piped water, but wished to use the same amount of water from wells, streams and boreholes, the water table would drop and would become polluted by sea water as has happened in Malta.

Today the demand is enormous. It has doubled since 1964, but the water caught in reservoirs is water which would have flowed into the sea. Jersey is not remotely short of water, but it was short of storage capacity until Queen's Valley reservoir was built.

The Island has 33 inches of rain per year. One inch of rain equals 100 tons of water to the acre, so each acre of ground in the Island receives 3,300 tons of water. Most of it runs into the sea. We lose a lot through evaporation in the summer.

We can use water but we cannot use it up. The water we use in the bathroom or washing the car, goes into the drains and into the sea, to be cleansed and caught up again by the atmosphere to fall as rain. In theory, the cup of water which we drink today, we could drink again next year. It is called the water-cycle. There is the same amount of water and water vapour in the world as there was in the days of Noah. If we lost water through using it, we could work out by computer when the world would end.

Today 80% of houses in the Island are on piped water, which means that we are using water which would have run into the sea. The water table which supplied the people before the waterworks existed, is mostly drawn on for irrigation.

HIGHEST DAILY DEMAND OF THE YEAR

Year		Millions of gallons
1939	23 August	1,285
1944	8 August	1,040
1949	20 June	1,470
1954	3 August	2,119
1959	15 June	2,554
1964	5 August	3,881
1969	8 August	4,250
1974	12 June	4,701
1979	26 July	4,890
1984	18 June	5,010
(1985	18 January	5,420)
1989	20 June	5,290
(1987	15 January	5,740)
1994	11 July	6,057

The huge demand in January 1985 and 1987, in brackets, was caused by frost and burst pipes. It equalled demand in high summer, and caused great anxiety.

AVERAGE RAINFALL FOR 123 YEARS

	Inches		Inches
January	3.47	July	1.98
February	2.60	August	2.24
March	2.50	September	2.77
April	2.02	October	3.84
May	1.99	November	4.20
June	1.80	December	4.03

One inch of rain equals 25.4 millimetres

ANNUAL RAINFALL FOR JERSEY FOR THE PAST 130 YEARS

Note that when the years are put into blocks of ten, the average rainfall has been never less than 30 inches or more than 36.42, giving an average of 33.31 inches.

The wettest three consecutive years were 1950, with 43.15 inches, 1951 with 42.19 inches and 1952 with 43.16 inches. Yet the 10-year block 1945-54 averaged 33.19 inches. Incidentally, 40 inches is 1,000 millimetres, so the wet years are easily seen.

This means that when we get three consecutive dry years, or three consecutive wet years, and begin to cast about us to see what has caused a change in climate, we need not fear. Nothing much has changed — the situation will average out.

The driest 10-year period is the latest — 1985-1994 with 30.32 inches, but 1895-1904 gave 30.65 inches, so the climate has not changed.

The hydrological year runs from 1 October to 30 September, and that is the basis of the figures. The year 1994 looks very dry with 25.96 inches, but it started on 1 October, 1993. The calendar year 1994 gave 41.36 inches — a very wet year — because October, November and December were abnormally wet. That will reflect on the Waterworks total for 1995.

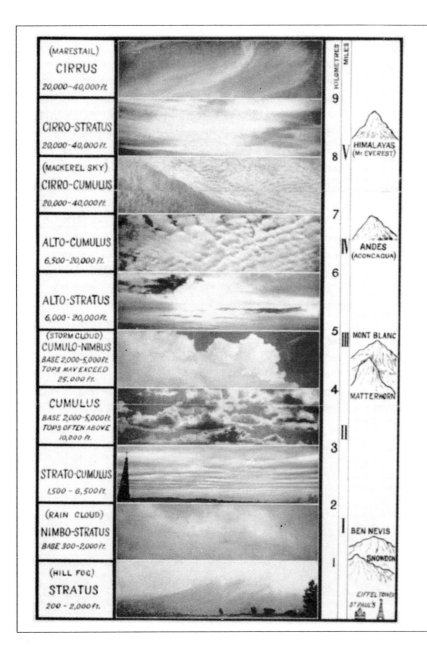

Forms, heights and names of clouds.

(MARESTAIL)
CIRRUS
20,000–40,000 ft.

CIRRO-STRATUS
20,000–40,000 ft.

(MACKEREL SKY)
CIRRO-CUMULUS
20,000–40,000 ft.

ALTO-CUMULUS
6,500–20,000 ft.

ALTO-STRATUS
6,000–20,000 ft.

(STORM CLOUD)
CUMULO-NIMBUS
BASE 2,000–5,000 ft.
TOPS MAY EXCEED
25,000 ft.

CUMULUS
BASE 2,000–5,000 ft.
TOPS OFTEN ABOVE
10,000 ft.

STRATO-CUMULUS
1,500–6,500 ft.

(RAIN CLOUD)
NIMBO-STRATUS
BASE 300–2,000 ft.

(HILL FOG)
STRATUS
200–2,000 ft.

KILOMETRES
MILES

9

8   V   HIMALAYAS
         (Mt EVEREST)

7

    IV ANDES
6   (ACONCAGUA)

5   III MONT BLANC

4   MATTERHORN

    II
3

2

    I   BEN NEVIS
        SNOWDON

        EIFFEL TOWER
        St PAUL'S

24

OBSERVING THE WEATHER

THOSE WHO HAVE never bothered to observe the weather, but would like to think about doing so should start by buying a wall barometer if there is not already one in the house. If two barometers are sold in St. Helier, one to a customer living in Trinity and another on the coast road at Samares, it should, regardless of location, be set to the sea level pressure, the instrument in Trinity will read lower. The barometer should be read in the morning and the gold hand should be moved to cover the black hand. When it is read in the evening it will be seen how much it has risen or fallen. Again the gold hand should cover the black. If there are violent movements it will probably be windy.

Generally speaking, but with many exceptions, it is basically fine when pressure is high, and unsettled when it is low. High is 1020 millibars and above, and low is 1000 millibars, 29.5 and below. You can get dull weather — 'anti-cyclonic gloom' in a high, especially in winter, and fair weather between showers when it is low, but experience teaches many things.

The next thing to observe is the direction and strength of the wind. If possible get a weather cock, or know where to see one. It is a help anyway because it indicates the points of the compass. It is surprising how often the wind changes in a day.

On many occasions a beach has been full of people bathing and building sandcastles in the sunshine. A black cloud appears and it gets darker and darker. Nobody moves until the first huge drops of rain associated with thunderstorms starts falling, and then there is a stampede. The observer would have gone ages before because he or she would know that the cloud is coming up with the wind. Some people have said, "Oh look at that black cloud," when the answer has to be "It has gone," because it is down-wind. The cloud normally moves in the same direction as the surface wind, but there are exceptions. When you lie in bed and see the clouds scudding over the moon, you should know the direction of the wind without looking at the wind vane. So it is important to know the points of the compass.

Let us now turn to a crucial factor in the lives of the people of Jersey, namely fog at the Airport. Every month there is a day or days when aircraft are delayed by what is called a 'clamp' — fog — so it does help to know a bit about it in order that one can prophesy when it might clear. Fog can stop all aircraft movements for several hours and, indeed, up to three days.

If the barometer is high and there is little wind and the sky is clear above, the odds are high that the sun will burn the fog off, starting in the east of the Island if the wind is west. Slight delay only. If it is a case of low cloud covering the Island — stratus — and the wind is strong, the sun will not appear and will not burn off the fog. If the sun did come out it could not burn off the cloud because the wind would instantly bring in cloud to cover anything that had been cleared. So a long wait. But there is hope. Watch the wind vane. If the wind is west, no hope. If it backs to south-west, or south of south-west, the cloud may be lifted to a hundred feet because of the shelter and drying-out over north-west France. It makes the difference between flying and not flying.

If the Island is in a warm sector with a trailing cold front and low barometer, it means drizzle and fog, and one can only gloomily peruse papers and books. There is no hope unless the cold front goes through ultimately, and the wind veers to north-west. This situation is when the clamp lasts for a day at least.

It is necessary to have the barometer reading in the head because there is always more chance of a clearance with high pressure than with low, and it is essential always to check the direction of the wind, bearing in mind that due west is the worst.

If you have access to a weather map, some of us were taught to watch Culdrose in Cornwall. If Culdrose clamps we shall clamp; if Culdrose clears, lift up your hearts!

Even those who are not flying suffer agony when the mail and papers aircraft are unable to land. It helps a bit to know if the chance of a later landing exists. Such delays affect many hundreds of people engaged in the distribution of newspapers and mail, and is very costly.

An observer should always know the times of high and low water, and whether it is a spring or a neap tide. This is because he or she knows that the height of the barometer greatly affects the height of the tide. A very low barometer can add two feet to high water, not counting the strength of the wind. Jersey is exceptional because of its tidal range, and is one of the highest in the world at 40 feet – 12.2 metres.

It is also necessary to note the sea temperature because there is little chance of snow lying if the sea temperature is in double figures. A January reading is normally around 8°C / 46°F.

The next thing to consider is the temperature, so one should buy a maximum/minimum thermometer, and put it in the shade facing north so that it is never in the sun. The maximum should be shaken down each morning, or pulled with a magnet, and the minimum set each morning. It is good to keep a record of the weather in a diary or weather chart. If not, it is difficult to remember dates of storm, snow or floods.

Finally, there is a rain gauge. It should be set well away from buildings so that it is not sheltered. Rain should be measured every morning at 9 a.m. GMT if possible with all the other readings.

There are various things that one can do such as noting visibility and the height and type of cloud, but the above is just a start. It is appreciated that it is not always possible to have instruments when there is no garden.

For those who have many friends to give presents one can advance from a wall barometer to a barograph. That traces a line showing the barometric pressure, and one can see at a glance what is happening. It is a noble piece of furniture but rather expensive. And if there are sufficient friends to make a present of a Stevenson Screen, that is another huge advance. That would contain a maximum-minimum thermometer as well as a dry and wet bulb for humidity, and a grass minimum thermometer. But there must be a garden.

The final advance for a senior observer would be an ane-mometer. That will give the speed of the wind as well as the direction. That is important as wind is a very destructive force. It is surprising how many fierce gusts there are in a storm, or when there are squalls.

An observer should also note when there is a solar or lunar halo – that is, a ring round the sun or moon. It is not a ring which almost touches the sun or moon, but is a fair way away. Normally 22°. One should cover the sun with the hand if it is too bright, and the large ring should be clearly seen. It nor-mally occurs when there is cirro-stratus, a smooth white high cloud formed of ice crystals which reduces the sunshine.
A lunar halo mostly occurs at or near the full moon. Almost certain rain follows a day or so afterwards. They are fairly rare.

Three successive ground frosts are often followed by rain. Excellent visibility usually indicates rain. When we had the brilliant summers of 1989 and 1990 it was very rare indeed to see the coast of France. There was always a heat haze. The best visibility is when the wind is between south-west and north-west when the air comes off the sea. A wind between north-east and south-east brings the smoke and pollution of the Continent, and dry air from the land mass. It is also the coldest quarter in the winter and the warmest in summer, so an easterly wind can be cold or hot according to the season.

Observers who study the States Meteorological Office annual report will find that the average summer is worse than we expect and the average winter is better than we expect. The summers of 1975, '76, '89 and '90 were freaks. They were exceptionally good, and the grown-ups of the future will tell of the wonderful summers they had when the were young.

A drought is 15 consecutive days without rain, and is fairly rare. So anyone having a fortnight's holiday must expect rain at times. For those who are lucky, it falls at night. On the other hand the chance of a severe winter is remote. There is very little snow in Jersey, and we get through winters without real trouble. When we have snow and burst pipes it generates the greatest indignation, except among the young. A toboggan may as well live in the loft. But its day will come.

Experience will show that the weather tends to repeat itself. It will start raining at roughly the same time each day for a long time. It gets into a slot, and it will come back to the same slot even if it loses if for a time. If we take the recent past we shall remember that November 1994 was the mildest since 1649. But December was mild, and so was January and February. We had nothing but rain, drizzle, cloud and strong winds caused by a series of depressions. Floods in Britain and Europe were abnormal.

There can be whole summers of brilliant weather and whole summers disastrously wet; whole summers of wet and mud and whole winters of bitter cold like 1962-63. If one is going on holiday in August, and it is wet in May and June, it is natural to assume that July, or at least August, will be fine. But the odds are that they will both be wet because the longer a type goes on the more likely it is to continue.

Whatever weather we record we always find that it has occurred before. 'The wettest year since ...'; 'the coldest winter since ...' Ecclesiastes chapter 3 verse 15 says 'that which hath been is now; and that which is to be hath already been.' We might remember that in the days of Joseph there were seven years of plenty and seven years of famine. If we had anything like that we should be saying that there has been a dramatic change of climate. In fact there are few signs of a change of climate this century. Global warming means the whole earth, not just one country, and there is little sign of it. It could only take place if the output of the sun increased, and nobody has ever found that out. One of the miracles is that the earth receives, on average, exactly the same amount of heat to one degree in spite of solar flares and enormous upheavals on the sun.

WEATHER MAPS

THERE ARE MANY types of weather maps. Some are for the surface and some are for the upper air. Some show places having the same pressure, and some show places having the same temperature.

Charts showing weather observations taken at the same time over an area are called 'synoptic charts.' In technical meteorological terms a current chart showing the pressure pattern (highs and lows) and associated 'fronts' is called Baratic. A chart which attempts to forecast the position, say, 24 hours ahead, is called a 'Prebaratic.' At present forecast charts up to five days ahead are available in main meteorological offices.

The lines shown on the maps are called isobars, and they join places having the same barometric pressure. They show the low pressure — depressions, and the high pressure — anticyclones. The air flows anti-clockwise round a low, slightly inwards, and clockwise round a high, slightly outwards. It is very helpful to learn this by heart. Young people should be tested thus:

1	Low pressure over Ireland.	*Answer:* south wind
2	High to the north and low to the south.	*Answer:* East
3	High to the east.	*Answer:* south
4	Low over Jersey.	*Answer:* light variable
5	Low over Belgium.	*Answer:* north
6	Low over Scotland.	*Answer:* west
7	Low over Paris.	*Answer:* east
8	High to the west.	*Answer:* north

It is necessary to shut the eyes and see the map in the mind's eye. The answers are not precise. A high to the west is more likely to give a north-west wind because the wind blows slightly outwards with a high.

The heavy black lines are called fronts. They mark the boundary between air masses of different origin. If air from the north pole meets air from the south of the north Atlantic a depression will form and rain and gales will be generated. One breeding ground is the Iceland area.

If the warm air is advancing its leading edge will be called a warm front and is shown on the map with 'blobs.' The leading edge of advancing cold air is called a cold front and is shown with 'spikes.'

Let us take a typical depression moving towards Ireland. The first sign is cirrus cloud at least a day in advance. They look like mares' tails and are around 30,000 feet. Then cirro-stratus, a smooth white high cloud. This lowers to alto-stratus and is medium cloud around 12,000 feet. One looks for a solar and lunar halo with cirro-stratus and alto-stratus.

Then the cloud lowers to stratus as the rain comes in.

The continuous moderate rain is ahead of a warm front. Once the front is through the rain turns to drizzle in what is called the warm sector. The drizzle turns to rain as the cold front goes through but there should be a chink of light in the west as the thick cloud which darkens with the front, gives way to a blue sky followed by showers and bright intervals. Sometimes the cold front does not go through because the warm air kicks back for a while. It is called a wave and it prolongs the drizzle and often causes a forecast to go wrong — "You said it would clear up and it didn't."

Sometimes the cold front doesn't get through at all. It is

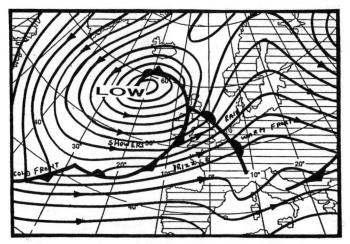

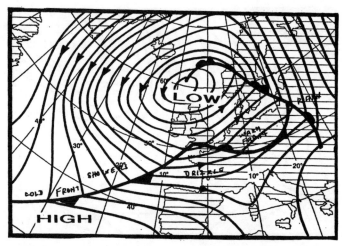

MAP 1   Shows a typical depression off north-west Scotland. The Channel Islands are in a warm sector with drizzle. The wind would be south-west strong to gale. There is rain ahead of the warm front and showers behind the cold front. However, the cold front looks as if it will not get through because there is a wave which might develop into a secondary depression.

MAP 2   Much the same situation with drizzle and warm sector conditions. Incidentally, relatively humidity is mostly around 100% in a warm sector. The original warm front is over Germany with the rain ahead of it. The cold front failed to go through because of a wave depression over Devon. Jersey may have been in warm moist air for two days with fog possibly affecting the Airport. The cold front looks as if it will go through in a couple of hours.

---

called a trailing cold front which oscillates, sometimes returning northwards as a warm front. It leaves Jersey in drizzle while southern England gets a clearance and bright sunshine, but it is tedious to discuss all the things that can go wrong. However, in summer at least, stratus cloud can burn off and give brilliant sunshine and high temperatures. That often happens with sea fog.

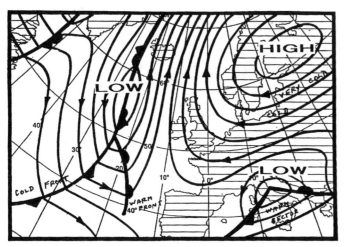 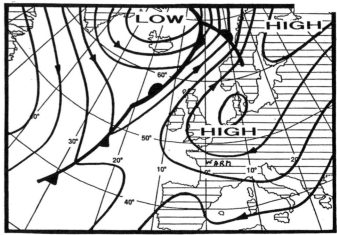

MAP 3   This is the fatal January situation with a high over Scandinavia and a low over Italy. Jersey would be getting an easterly wind and severe frost. The low to the west of Britain would move north, but what is called the blocking high would stop it bringing in rain or snow. This is a high to the north and a low to the south situation. It can stick for a long time as it did in 1946-47 and 1962-63. In both those cases there was high pressure over Siberia, Iceland and Greenland. It is something to look for in the winter. A high to the south and low to the north is a westerly situation and therefore relatively mild, and is more usual. Map 3 shows a very cold Europe.

MAP 4   This is a summer situation, giving fine warm weather. The wind would be east, light to moderate. An easterly wind from the Continent is cold in winter and warm in summer. That goes for south-east as well. The front to the west would not affect us because of the blocking high. Humidity would be low. A westerly wind would keep the temperature down because it would be passing over sea which would have a temperature around 18°C (64°F).

'SUNNY JERSEY'

JERSEY IS THE SUNNIEST PLACE in the British Isles. This is acknowledged officially by the Meteorological Office, Dunstable, and by the Royal Meteorological Society.

Bright sunshine is recorded by a Campbell-Stokes sunshine recorder. This is a glass sphere mounted on a stand. A special card records burns, and these burns appear even when the card is wet. There are three different cards according to the season and therefore the angle of the sun. One for summer; one for winter and one for spring and autumn.

The Jersey station at Fort Regent is the most southerly in the British Isles, and it is not surprising that it wins. There are two other stations in the Island, one at the Airport and the other at Mont Orgueil Castle. In the long term, Fort Regent is the most favourable site.

It may not be appreciated that a telephone pole getting in the way of the recorder can knock two minutes a day off the sunshine total. That is 730 minutes a year, or 12 hours. As we only beat the Isle of Wight and Bognor Regis by a few hours in a year, the perfect site is essential.

When Guernsey Airport reported their sunshine, it did not threaten us, but when their report came from L'Ancresse, it became a deadly rival and sometimes beat us. Jersey is by no means top every year, but is the leading station one year in three or four. No other station can equal that. We have always been in the top ten stations, and again, that in itself is a record.

A word about bright sunshine. If you can look at the sun without blinking and getting tears in the eyes, it is not recording. That is normally before sunset and after sunrise when the sun appears as a red ball. But it is also when there is cirrostratus and altostratus causing what we call a watery sun. It does not burn on the card and therefore does not count. So a fine dry day when the sun's disc can be seen does not mean that it is a sunny day.

We often lose half an hour of sunshine after sunrise and half an hour before sunset due to dust in the atmosphere. The best situation is behind a cold front, with excellent visibility. It is then difficult driving a car into the setting sun because of the glare. In June it is possible to record 15.6 hours of sunshine in a day.

Every part of the world has an average of 12 hours of light and 12 hours of darkness daily throughout the year. But the distribution varies. At the Equator there is not much difference between winter and summer. At the north and south Poles there is 24 hours of darkness in winter and 24 hours of daylight in summer. It is possible to record nearly 24 hours of sunshine in the summer in a day.

It follows, therefore, that, oddly enough, Jersey is capable of recording more sunshine than England or Scotland in winter, and less than England and Scotland in summer. This is because it gets darker going north in winter and lighter going north in summer. But when all is said and done, any place in England and Scotland can beat Jersey in sunshine, because every place has an equal chance as the sun is above the horizon on average 12 hours a day. We can record 15.6 hours of sunshine in June, but north Scotland 17 hours. We can get nearly 8 hours of sunshine in December, but north Scotland about 5 hours.

SUN TIMES IN JERSEY

Latest sunset:	9.21 BST (Constant 21 June to 30 June)
Latest sunrise:	8.04 GMT on 4 January
Earliest sunset:	4.11 GMT on 10 December
Earliest sunrise:	5.03 on 21 June
Longest day:	21 June
Shortest day:	21 December

Note that the earliest sunset is on 10 December and the latest sunrise is on 4 January. The shortest day is 21 December. This is because on 11 December the sun sets half a minute later, but rises one minute later so giving a shorter day. On 22 December the sun sets one minute later and rises half a minute later, so the day is longer. That is why people say on Christmas Day, "I already notice that the days are longer." Yes. sunset has been later since 11 December. Longest and shortest days can vary slightly because of leap years.

THE MOON

I am often asked if it is true that the moon is up in the daytime. The answer is that it is up as much in the day as it is in the night, but it is not easily visible because of cloud or bright sunshine.

The new moon, a thin crescent, is near to the sun at sunset, and so is seen setting soon after dark. A week later it has waxed to half a moon known as the first quarter. It is then at its highest point in the sky — apogee — at sunset. It rises later each day as high tide is later, and a week after that it is full moon, and it rises as the sun sets, and sets as the sun rises. The last half moon, or last quarter, rises so late that it is at its highest point as the sun rises. After that it is in the sky all day, until, as new moon, it is setting with the sun.

The moon is 239,000 miles away and the sun is 93,000,000 miles away. Sometimes one gets in the way of another and there is an eclipse. Solar eclipses occur only when the moon is new, and lunar eclipses only when the moon is full.

SUNSHINE IN JERSEY

Space prevents the printing of each year's results for the last 30 years, so a random selection only has been taken. Perhaps the most interesting year was 1981 when Scotland and northern England beat us hollow. It proves that any station in the British Isles can be top. We start with the sunniest stations in each month for 1960 followed by the top 20 stations. Note that 1989 and 1990 were very sunny years.

The last list, showing the number of times each station appears in the top ten is the most important. Guernsey Airport was never top of the top ten, but Guernsey L'Ancresse was top five times. That is more than any station other than Jersey.

The sunniest stations in each month were as follows:-

1970

	Name	Hours
1.	Shanklin	1951
2.	Eastbourne	1917
3.	Swanage	1904
4.	**Jersey, St. Helier**	1887
5.	Ventnor	1880
6.	Worthing	1865
7.	Guernsey, L'Ancresse	1856
8.	Bognor	1898
9.	Weymouth	1849
10.	Bournemouth	1848

1972

1.	Ventnor	1844
2.	Shanklin	1816
3.	Guernsey L'Ancresse	1793
4.	Sandown	1789
5.	**Jersey, St. Helier**	1788
6.	Bognor	1765
7.	Exmouth	1753
8.	Dale Fort, Pembroke	1748
9.	Eastbourne	1726
10.	Torquay	1723

1973

1.	**Jersey, St. Helier**	2003
2.	Guernsey, L'Ancresse	2001
3.	**Jersey, Gorey Castle**	1981
4.	Shanklin	1959
5.	Sandown	1942
6.	Ventnor	1930
7.	**Jersey Airport**	1925
8.	Eastbourne	1919
9.	Bognor	1878
10.	Brighton	1876

1975

	Name	Hours
1.	Guernsey, L'Ancresse	2097
2.	**Jersey, St. Helier**	2077
3.	**Jersey Airport**	1995
4.	**Jersey, Gorey Castle**	1974
5.	Guernsey Airport	1960
6.	Bournemouth	1959
7.	Sandown	1956
8.	Shanklin	1943
9.	Torquay	1927
10.	Poole	1914

1976

1.	**Jersey, St. Helier**	2155
2.	Shanklin	2129
3.	Guernsey, L'Ancresse	2111
4.	Eastbourne	2102
5.	**Jersey, Gorey Castle**	2098
6.	Sandown	2076
7.	**Jersey Airport**	2074
8.	Hastings	2055
9.	Ventnor	2040
10.	Folkestone	2040

1978

1.	Guernsey, L'Ancresse	1881
2.	**Jersey, St. Helier**	1879
3.	Torbay	1854
4.	**Jersey, Gorey Castle**	1833
5.	Penzance	1827
6.	Shanklin	1824
7.	The Lizard, Cornwall	1798
8.	**Jersey Airport**	1785
9.	Prawle Point, Devon	1764
10.	Guernsey Airport	1757

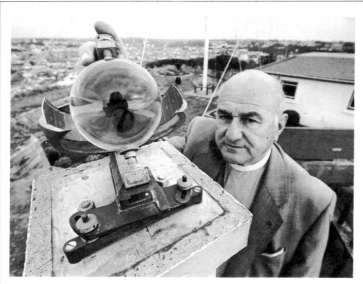

The most precious meteorological instrument: Jersey's sunshine recorder at Fort Regent Signal Station.

Fracto-cumulus cloud over St. Clement's Bay looking from Noirmont Point to Green Island.
(Photo by Reg Quérée).

1979		
	Name	**Hours**
1.	Guernsey, L'Ancresse	1878
2.	Shanklin	1856
3.	Torbay	1845
4.	**Jersey, St. Helier**	1831
5.	Bognor	1821
6.	Hayling Island	1796
7.	**Jersey, Gorey Castle**	1792
8.	Eastbourne	1779
9.	Littlehampton	1776
10.	Portland Bill	1776

1981		
1.	Leuchars Fife, Scotland	1634
2.	Boulmer, Northumberland	1618
3.	St. Andrews, Scotland	1593
4.	Guernsey, L'Ancresse	1592
5.	Dunbar, East Lothian, Scotland	1590
6.	Abroath, Scotland	1588
7.	**Jersey, St. Helier**	1586
8.	Shanklin	1579
9.	Tynemouth	1564
10.	Hayling Island	1555

1982		
1.	Folkestone	1893
2.	Bognor	1885
3.	**Jersey, St. Helier**	1878
4.	Eastbourne	1878
5.	Hastings	1861
6.	Bexhill	1845
7.	Hayling Island	1836
8.	Herstmonceux, East Sussex	1835
9.	**Jersey Airport**	1833
10.	Worthing	1818

1983		
	Name	**Hours**
1.	Bognor	1897
2.	**Jersey, St. Helier**	1861
3.	Folkestone	1861
4.	Hayling Island	1853
5.	**Jersey Airport**	1837
6.	Sandown	1822
7.	Herstmonceux, East Sussex	1811
8.	**Jersey, Gorey Castle**	1795
9.	Worthing	1792
10.	Shanklin	1790

1989		
1.	**Jersey, St. Helier**	2249
2.	Guernsey, L'Ancresse	2231
3.	**Jersey Airport**	2198
4.	**Jersey, Gorey Castle**	2185
5.	Guernsey Airport	2182
6.	Bognor	2166
7.	Hayling Island	2110
8.	Folkestone	2102
9.	Eastbourne	2094
10.	Bournemouth	2090

1990		
1.	Bognor	2242
2.	Folkestone	2217
3.	Herne Bay	2176
4.	**Jersey, St. Helier**	2171
5.	**Jersey Airport**	2165
6.	Guernsey, L'Ancresse	2149
7.	**Jersey, Gorey Castle**	2148
8.	Guernsey Airport	2137
9.	Eastbourne	2135
10.	Worthing	2109

The number of times each station appears in the top ten stations in 30 years is as follows. The figure in brackets is the number of times the station was top of the top ten:-

1.	**Jersey, St. Helier, Fort Regent**	(11)	30
2.	Guernsey, L'Ancresse	(5)	26
3.	**Jersey, Gorey Castle**	(2)	24
4.	**Jersey Airport**	(0)	21
5.	Shanklin	(5)	21
6.	Bognor Regis	(4)	20
7.	Eastbourne	(0)	20
8.	Sandown	(0)	16
9.	Guernsey Airport	(0)	15
10.	Hayling Island	(0)	12
11.	Ventnor	(1)	12

The above table is the most important of all. It shows that Jersey was in the top ten stations 30 times in 30 years and top of the top ten on 11 occasions.

Bognor Regis was in the top ten 20 times in 30 years, and was top of the top ten on 4 occasions.

HUMIDITY

Average relative humidity as recorded at St. Louis Observatory at 9 a.m. is as follows:-

January	85%
February	82%
March	79%
April	75%
May	73%
June	73%
July	73%
August	75%
September	77%
October	81%
November	82%
December	81%

Relative humidity expresses the amount of moisture in the atmosphere as a percentage of what it is capable of holding. When the atmosphere can hold no more there is 100% humidity and mist, cloud, rain or drizzle occurs. It means that the air temperature has reached the 'dew point.' The dry bulb and the wet bulb read the same.

On the grass under a clear sky with no wind, the temperature easily drops to the dew point and dew forms. If the temperature drops below freezing, white frost (hoar frost) forms.

As the Island is surrounded by sea, it gets a lot of moist air with the humidity at or near 100%, especially in warm sectors. On the other hand, dry continental air gives us humidity nearer 50%. It will be seen that the average humidity in the spring and summer is in the seventies and is in the low eighties in the autumn and winter.

High humidity causes damp and is bad for those with rheumatism, but most of the year the air is surprisingly dry.

THE BEAUFORT WIND SCALE

The Beaufort Wind Scale was devised in 1805 by Admiral Beaufort.

Notation	Nos. 0-12	MPH	Effects produced on land
Calm	0	0-1	Calm; smoke rises vertically
Light air	1	1-3	Direction of wind shown by smoke drift but not by wind vanes
Slight breeze	2	4-7	Wind felt on face; leaves rustle; ordinary vane moved by wind
Gentle breeze	3	8-12	Leaves and small twigs in constant motion; wind extends light flag
Moderate breeze	4	13-18	Raises dust and loose leaves; small branches are moved
Fresh breeze	5	19-24	Small trees in leaf begin to sway; crested wavelets on inland waters
Strong breeze	6	25-31	Large branches moving; whistling of telegraph wires; umbrellas difficult
Moderate gale	7	32-38	Whole trees in motion; hard walking against wind
Gale	8	39-46	Breaks twigs off trees; traffic disturbed
Strong gale	9	47-54	Slight structural damage (chimney pots and slates)
Whole gale	10	55-63	Seldom experienced inland; trees uprooted; structural damage
Storm	11	64-75	Very rarely experienced; accompanied by widespread damage
Hurricane	12	Greater than 75	

Route Orange, St. Brelade's, before the storm of November 1987. It occurred in the small hours at high water neap tide. Incredibly, nobody was killed. (Photo Jersey Evening Post.)

The southerly wind gusting over 100 miles per hour (and over 130 mph in parts of Normandy and Brittany) brought down thousands of trees in Jersey and over a million on the mainland, including many at Kew Gardens. Had the wind been west it would have done little damage as trees grow to cope with westerlies. Many people did not know the houses existed at Route Orange because had been hidden by the trees. (Photo Jersey Evening Post.)

THE PROBLEM OF LANGUAGE

A KEY PROBLEM facing forecasters daily is giving a forecast which accurately conveys what they think will happen, and which registers with the people listening or reading.

Many people don't connect because they don't listen throughout the forecast, and then forget what they heard. The words 'risk of a shower' provokes the remark, 'they say it will rain.' That is the last thing the forecaster wanted to convey. He or she probably meant that it would be a fine day, but in the odd place there was a risk of a shower. Not that there would be a shower, but just a risk.

Forecasters as a breed have always preferred to mention rain even if it is only a risk. They are not worried if it doesn't rain. But they hate to predict a fine day and have it rain. Perhaps it is because people notice if it is that way round.

It is interesting to ponder how forecasters would have worded a forecast after the event. How would yesterday's forecast have been worded in the light of what happened so as to convey the weather accurately to the country?

The limited time on television virtually destroys the forecaster. Some are cut off only for trailers of future programmes to be shown. It does not register in high places that some forecasts are easy; 'fine and warm throughout the country' almost sums it up. Other situations are complex with many variations across the country and with England, Scotland, Wales and Northern Ireland needing a forecast of its own. How can this be done in two minutes? Consider an incident in Jersey which occurred on 12 June, 1993.

Driving east from St. Helier about 6 p.m. one noticed a black cloud over Gorey. It started raining at Le Hocq, and it became heavy at La Rocque and violent at Gorey. A call to the Met. Office informed the forecaster that 15 millimetres had been recorded at Gorey in the last hour. None had fallen at the Airport. An hour later there were 50 millimetres at La Planque, Gorey Village, and one millimetre at the Airport. In the end 3 inches of rain or 75 millimetres were recorded at Archirondel where £40,000 of damage was done to a house. A car was overturned, and books and silver were found on the beach. Water had flooded down the hill.

So what should the forecast have been for Jersey? And what for the Channel Islands? Guernsey had nothing. It was a thunderstorm off Cherbourg which just scraped the east of Jersey.

At this point it is worth mentioning that forecasters tend to play down thunderstorms because many people are terrified at the mention of the word. Hence, 'the odd rumble of thunder' — and then hastening on to the direction of the wind or temperature. Thunder is noise and cannot hurt anyone — it is the sound of the flash of lightning. So anyone who hears thunder is safe. If a person is struck by lightning they won't hear the thunder! Children should be taught to calculate how far away the lightning is. Stand by the window and count the number of seconds that the thunder is heard after the flash. Sound travels at one mile every five seconds — very slow. Light travels at 186,000 miles a second. So if there is a ten second gap between the flash and the thunder the storm is two miles away. If there is a vivid flash and an instant bang of thunder, the storm is almost in the back garden. Let it be a comfort that hardly anyone has been killed in Jersey by lightning this century.

On another occasion it started raining on Battle of Flowers day of all days, but stopped at noon. We got away with it. But it rained all afternoon in Guernsey. So what should the forecast have been for the Channel Islands? Quite often people mutter that the weather forecast was wrong for Jersey when it was probably right for Guernsey. Fog sometimes afflicts one island but not both, so somebody grumbles. We might remember that the rainfall varies greatly in Britain, the west having far more than the east. A glance at the various rainfall tables in the daily papers show great differences. Even in Jersey the average rainfall at St. John is 33 inches, but only 26 inches for La Rocque — one quarter less.

Masters of ships and air pilots are among those who can tune in to the problems of forecasters, and be well acquainted with the variables of language. Some people sneer at gale warnings, and point out that the wind has never touched force 8. But those sailing the Channel will testify that the wind at sea is very different to that on land. And the wind and sea on the west coast of Jersey in a west wind is very different to the east coast. And vice versa with an east wind.

Here is a list of some of the words we hear on radio and television. I welcome such expressions as 'bits and pieces of rain or drizzle' as it is a relief to get away from formal language. None of this is a criticism but the question has to be asked as to whether people are able to differentiate between 'fair' and 'mainly fair', and understand the general inference giving highs and lows, and can recognise a lunar halo. There is a case of having a competition in the family to see how many of the 100 expressions are fully understood (see facing column).

A student should know the difference between occasional showers and scattered showers. Occasional showers means that there will be a shower from time to time. Scattered showers means that there will be showers in a few districts, but not necessarily in the student's area.

A shower means a shower of rain. A wintry shower means that it is likely to be of sleet, snow or hail. A drought is a period of no rain lasting for at least 15 consecutive days. And so on.

Freezing rain
Periods of rain
Occasional rain
Scattered rain
Local rain
Intermittent rain
Bits and pieces
  of rain or drizzle
Showers
Local showers

Scattered showers
Occasional showers
The odd shower
Light shower
Wintry shower
Rain turning to
  showers
Fine
Fair
Mainly fair
Dull
Murky
Gloomy
Waterspout
Sun Pillar
Beaufort scale
Mercury barometer
Barograph

Aneroid barometer
Isobars
Blizzard
Monsoon
Drought
Cold front
Warm front
Occlusion
Trough of low pressure

Depression
Anti-cyclone
Anti-cyclonic gloom
Ridge of high pressure
Polar low
Col
Whole gale

Storm
Hurricane

Tempest
Tornado
Tropical storm
Typhoon
Sirocco
Trade winds

Mistral
Squall
Line squall
Gust
Dust storm
Ice crystals
Tropopause
Dry bulb
Wet bulb
Relative humidity
Dew point

Hygrometer
Lunar halo
Solar halo
Cirrus
Cirro-stratus
Altocumulus
Altocumulus castellatus
Altocumulus lenticularis
Altostratus

Cumulonimbus
Stratus
Haar
Hoar frost
Air frost
Ground frost
Rime

Minimum temperature
Grass minimum
  temperature
Fog
Freezing fog
Ground fog
Radiation fog
Sea fog
Local fog

Haze
Mist
Sheet lightning
Forked lightning
Thunderbolt
Odd rumble of thunder
Local thunder
Distant lightning
Tropical maritime air
Dry Continental air
Automatic weather
  station
Arctic region
Antarctic region
Weather ship

A student of 12 years of age should get 30 correct answers.
A student of 15 years of age should get 80 correct answers.

THE SHIPPING AND OTHER FORECASTS

COASTAL STATION REPORTS
Given in the Shipping Forecasts

Tiree (T)   Stornoway (S)
Sumbrugh (Su)   Fifeness (F)
Bridlington (Br)   Dover (D)
Greenwich Light Vessel automatic (G)
Jersey (J)
Channel Light Vessel automatic (C)
Scilly automatic (Sc)   Valentia (V)
Ronaldsway (R)   Malin Head (M)

The fatal word 'automatic' means that the station gives wind
speed and direction, visibility and barometric pressure. It does
not give weather, i.e. meaning continuous moderate rain,
snow, thunderstorms or showers. As Greenwich Light Vessel
automatic and the Isles of Scilly are west of us where weather
usually comes from, it is a disaster as the stations are vital. Also
automatic are Dinard and Cap de la Hague.

BROADCASTING WEATHER
The shipping forecast goes out on Radio 4 Long Wave at 0033,
0555, 1355 and 1850.
Arguably the best forecast of the week is the one following the
farming programme at 1255 on BBC1 television (on Sundays).
It is a 5-day forecast. Watch that and you have a fair idea of
what the week will be like. If that is missed, there is a 5-day
forecast at about 0617 in the middle of the farming
programme on Radio 4 on Mondays.
All the above times are liable to change.

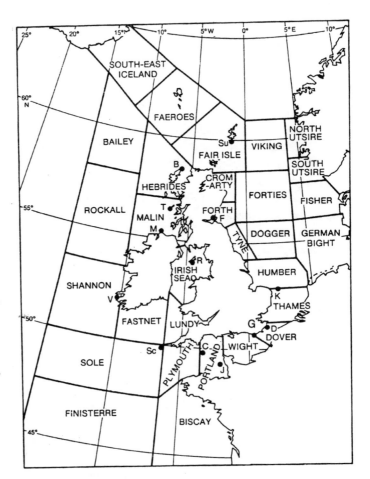

Shipping Map.

LA CORBIERE LIGHTHOUSE

BECAUSE OF ROCKS and huge tides, the Channel Islands have been a graveyard for ships for many centuries, and towards the end of the last century lighthouses were built at the Casquets, Hanois off Guernsey and La Corbière, Jersey. The building of the latter is worth a note.

The first recorded wreck off La Corbière was that of a Spanish ship on 25 November, 1495, and is mentioned in the *Chroniques de Jersey* which were compiled anonymously in 1585. It states that the sands were saturated with wine, and even the hall of St. Ouen's Manor 'lay almost filled with barrels of wine' on the Feast of St. Catherine.

The law known as *Droit de varech* or 'Wreckage Rights' meant that both ship and its cargo became the property of the Seigneur of the area.

Although Mons. A. G. Cluveaux in his guide book of 1876 says that 'the savage Islanders of Quennevais lure ships to their doom by fixing lanterns to the horns of their cows'; the humanising and civilising effects of Christianity, plus the fact that trade was in full swing between Jersey, Newfoundland and England, made safety at sea of paramount importance. A petition was sent to the Lords Commissioners of Her Majesty's Privy Council for Trade on 29 September, 1857, urging the establishment of a lighthouse at La Corbière.

After much debate in the States, the Rev. Le Couteur Balleine, Rector of St. Mary, proposed that Trinity House should build and maintain the lighthouse, but it was defeated by 19 votes to 13. In the event, the design by Sir John Coode, the famous harbours engineer, was accepted, with R. Imrie Bell, the executive engineer to the States, supervising his work.

On 16 May, 1873, work was started, and by November 1873, both the lighthouse and causeway were completed.

This incredibly quick effort was made possible by the fact that all materials and supplies were brought by ship to an adjacent rock because there was no road, only a track, to La Corbière. Even so, the foundation was cut out of solid rock, and the building was of concrete, the first concrete lighthouse in the British Isles.

Workshops, stores and a concrete mixing platform were built on a patch of rocks 80 yards from the tower being built. Barges and a steam tug brought a constant stream of materials, including gravel, sand and cement. These were carried by an overhead rope railway suspended between two rocks. The carriage consisted of a single wheel with a grooved tyre, which travelled on the rope, supporting a block and tackle carrying the bag or basket of material. This wheel with tackle was pulled along the ropeway by a small endless wire rope wound round a drum, worked with a small windlass by two men.

The official opening took place on 1 June, 1874, when the Bailiff, Mr. John Hammond, with the President and members of the Harbours Committee, went to the foot of the tower. Sir John Coode presented the key to Jurat Falle (the father of Lord Portsea) and the Dean, the Rev. W. C. Le Breton, M.A. (the father of Lillie Langtry), offered a short prayer. The light came on at sunset and could be seen for 18 miles, while the foghorn had a range of 4 miles.

Sir John Coode's fee was £462 1s. 6d. while that of Mr. Imrie Bell was £480. Neither received a penny. The matter came up in the States several times. On 4 April, 1879, five years after the work started, the House agreed by 21 votes to 9 to pay the fees. The lighthouse cost £2,976 to build, but the light, foghorn, causeway keepers' cottage and stores brought the total to £8,000.

The Admiralty was informed that 'the light is elevated at 119 feet above mean sea level of the high water spring tides at La Corbière Rock, Latitude 49° 10' 40" N., Longitude 2° 14' 50" W. All bearings are magnetic. Variation 19.5° westerly in 1874". (The 1995 magnetic variation is 4° 26 minutes, and it reduces 7 minutes annually).

On 31 October, 1933, the intensity of the beam of light was increased from 29,500 candles to 50,000 while occulting screens floating in a mercury bath and driven by clockwork enable a 5 second light and 5 seconds darkness to be perfectly displayed. The machinery was set in motion by Jurat G. F. B. de Gruchy of Noirmont Manor. He was already involved with the planning and building of the Airport which opened in 1937. His father was involved with the building of the railway from the Weybridge to La Corbière.

On 28 May, 1946, a Mr. and Mrs. S. Belsey, visitors to the Island, were sitting on a rock there and failed to note that it was being surrounded. The husband waded to the shore, but his wife, frightened, failed to respond to his signal to follow him. Mr. Peter Larbalestier, the assistant lighthouse keeper displayed great heroism by swimming out to her rescue and reached her. In attempting to bring her back to land, both were swept away by the strong current and perished — victims of the ruthless sea. A plaque is at the entrance to the cause-way. There are no keepers now at Corbière as the light is automatic.

That tragedy apart, the lighthouse has probably saved many ships and perhaps many hundreds of people in the 120 years of its existence. It is of great beauty and dignity, and is the most photographed place in the Island, and must rank as one of the most famous lighthouses in Britain. Every sailor leaving Guernsey is comforted by seeing the pinpoint light of La Corbière. It has never failed, but it lay in darkness during the German Occupation.

La Corbière has an occulting light. An occulting light means more light than darkness; a flashing light means more darkness than light.

The building of the lighthouse was a great event in the Island. Many ships went out to see it light up for the first time. The States' tug Duke of Normandy carried V.I.Ps. But no member of the Harbours Committee bothered to turn up.

At 10.05 hours on Easter Monday, 17 April, 1995, the red pennant was hoisted at Fort Regent Signal Station indicating the calling out of the lifeboat. Another yachtsman in trouble? At the same time the St. Helier Harbourmaster, Captain Roy Bullen, was telephoned at his La Rocque home asking him to go to the Harbour Office immediately. As he reached for his hat he glanced out of the window and saw a ship tearing across the Royal Bay of Grouville with smoke belching out of the funnels. He didn't need any second telling. He went.

It turned out that the French ferry St. Malo, with 307 passengers aboard, had struck a rock off La Corbière Light-house, and was sinking. An SOS had been sent out, and was responded to by the St. Helier and St. Catherine's lifeboats, the Condor 8, the Pegasus, the Amathus, the car ferry Solidor, the catamaran Trident 4, the Trident 5 and the car ferry Havelat. In addition there were several private boats and two helicopters.

In the event all the passengers were saved although 53, all elderly, were injured through jumping at least 12 feet. The St. Malo, which has 350 seats, is twin-hulled, and is an alumin-ium catamaran. Although severely holed on the port side, it did not sink, and was towed to St. Aubin's Bay, and later to St. Helier Harbour for repair, before being towed to Cherbourg.

The St. Malo, owned by the French Company Channiland, cost £3.5 million, and was under the Command of Captain Philippe Penau, a very experienced skipper. He took the ship through the Jailers' Passage which is 400 metres wide. It follows a path between the lighthouse and a group of rocks, and has been taken by a million ships since the lighthouse was built without any trouble. It does not mean going over the causeway of the lighthouse – that would be a different matter. Nor is it a short cut. The captain simply wished his passengers to have a close view of the famous lighthouse. It was an honourable intention, and is something which the majority of ships carrying foreign visitors do.

On this particular day, high water was at 0831 BST and was the highest tide of the year at 38.6 feet. The ship hit a rock called La Frouquie (see page 58), which is one third of a mile beyond the lighthouse and is in line with the centre of Petit Port. So the captain had cleared the Jailers' Passage, but had not turned to port quickly enough, possibly because of the swell and force 4 wind.

The ship left St. Helier at 0935 BST. Had he left at 0835 he would have cleared the rock because there would have been three feet more water. Had he left at 1035 there would have been six feet less water than at 0935 and the rock would have been visible. At least the waves would have been seen breaking over it. The tidal heights were as follows:

0831	38.6 feet
0935	35.6 feet
1035	29.6 feet
1135	20.6 feet

The rock is not covered at high water neaps, and is therefore visible for 85% of the time. On the highest tide of the year he would have most certainly cleared it, but not one hour later.

La Frouquie rock can be seen at any time other than high water springs from Petit Port Bay or half way up the hill. It is the twin-pointed rock far out in the centre of Petit Port.

The fact that the ship didn't sink after striking a rock at about 30 knots is a remarkable tribute to the catamaran. The fact that there was no loss of life is surely a tribute to the crew and the astonishing response of so many ships and aircraft. It speaks to us of the spirit between those who go down to the sea in ships. But there is more. There was the response of those on land. The injured were taken to hospital where off-duty doctors and nurses joined the duty staff, ambulances were waiting and officials of all sorts were there to comfort and help those who were soaked through but distressed though uninjured.

Many rehearsals were held to prepare for such an event. But the real thing was different. There were 175 Germans aboard, many of whom did not speak English; there were pregnant women and babies; there were some who had one arm or one leg, and were handicapped. All were saved.

It was the biggest accident since the war. The worst was during the Occupation when the *Schottland* struck the Grande Grune rocks off Noirmont on 5 January, 1943. Nearly all were drowned. The *SS Caesarea* struck the Petit Fours off Noirmont in fog on 7 July, 1923. All 373 passengers were rescued.

Nearly all the accidents were due to tide or weather.

THE CRANE 'HERCULES'

WHEN QUEEN VICTORIA laid the foundation stone of Victoria College, which was opened in 1852, Prince Albert asked why Jersey built its harbours on land. This was because they had to be ferried by little boats from the Royal Yacht. There was no such thing as a landing stage. Even when Victoria Pier was built, the entire harbour was empty at low water spring tide because there was no dredging then, and the States regarded dredging as unnecessary and costly. St. Helier was not a port before 1750.

A translation from the *Actes des Etats* for 26 February, 1869, states that:

1. There does not exist a landing stage at any of the harbours of St. Helier at low water.
2. Passengers are often compelled to embark or disembark in small boats, and are thereby subjected to serious inconvenience and to an additional expense.
3. Everyday, communications with England as well as with France become more frequent, while steamships bring larger numbers of travellers.
4. It is an advantage to the Island that there should be an increase in these communications by at least providing for these travellers all possible facilities of landing and re-imbarking.

All this suggests that Jersey was self-sufficient just over a hundred years ago, and didn't bother with people from England and France. St. Aubin was a secondary port, but that was virtually empty except for spring tides, and some ships had to wait for ten days if they missed the spring tide. Compare that with today with the harbour and airport, and the indignation felt if there is a delay of a few hours because of fog or gale, to the million passengers who travel each year.

There was a strong move for the building of a breakwater or harbour along the coastline from St. Aubin to Noirmont where deep water is always available. If this plan had been put into execution it would have shifted the mercantile centre from St. Helier to St. Aubin and made that town assume bigger, and perhaps more important, proportions. As it was, St. Aubin was the more important port before 1750. According to Balleine the States obtained permission to levy duties on wines and spirits in order to erect a pier at St. Aubin 'for the greater security of the merchants.' By 1668 merchants had begun to make cellars in the town, as St. Aubin was then called, to store their goods. The King's Scales, at what is now the Old Court House, was already in use to weigh all merchandise landed. The houses had their own private quays at the bottom of each garden. There was an open-air market on Mondays for merchants of foreign commodities. The pressure for Noirmont and St. Aubin was strengthened by the building of a railway from St. Helier to St. Aubin. That opened on 25 October, 1870, and closed temporarily on 26 October because part of the line had been washed away by a high spring tide, and before the sea wall had been completed. Note that the VIPs on the first day adjourned for refreshment to Noirmont Manor.

However, the lot fell to Mr. Coode, later Sir John, to design and build an enormous harbour from where the Electricity Station stands on reclaimed land at La Collette, to Elizabeth Castle, where a breakwater was to be built. Let it be said at this stage that the breakwater is arguably the finest building as a sea defence in the Island. It is smothered with foam at every south-westerly gale, and it faces huge waves and rollers from the Atlantic without frequent major maintenance. So does St. Catherine's Breakwater.

The plan was to build a pier from Pointe des Pas to the Platte Rock, so the harbour entrance would be at Elizabeth Castle breakwater. It is called Fort Elizabeth in *The Engineer* of 23 February, 1877. The plan also included a floating dock and graving dock. Fort Charles is also mentioned and the breakwater was supposed to be known as Charles.

A feature was the crane 'Hercules' on the breakwater. It could lift 120 tons and was much admired A crane on the mainland in 1995 was 640 feet high and could lift 1,200 tons. There was also the railway engine 'David'. However, a severe gale at Christmas, 1874, did a considerable amount of damage and the work was severely criticised in the States. Another in 1875 and a third in 1876 brought the work to a halt. The States cancelled the project, and what would have been a distinctive and notable harbour, at least up to that of Guernsey, was destroyed by the weather and tides.

The breakwater was half finished, and Hercules stood alone for ten years. Then the States decided to complete the breakwater, and Hercules started up first time. The point was made, and it is surely a valid one, that if the breakwater had been completed before the Pointe des Pas work started, the shelter would have saved the work.

Concrete was a new thing, and La Corbière lighthouse was the first lighthouse to have been built in concrete in the United Kingdom. It was under grave suspicion, and many felt that the failure of the work was due to the new-fangled stuff. They had certainly not heard of concrete degradation. The cement came from the Medina works in the Isle of Wight, a firm still running through and after the Second World War. There was also Portland stone. La Corbière concrete was very successful, but the States regarded it with suspicion.

A letter from the Rev. J. J. Balleine says,

'Granite sides and top-paving! Will this not be showing a brave exterior, whilst it conceals a rotten core? Our Breakwater will then give us an actual illustration in high relief of the old adage, 'the cowl does not always make the monk.' Since Concrete alone is now in favour with the powers that be, and the fiat has gone forth, that we are to have a Breakwater built of concrete blocks, laid upon a concrete bed, and swaddled in a granite overcoat ... '

Nevertheless, the second half of the breakwater is said to be the stronger. It is still there after 110 years, and St. Catherine's after nearly 150 years. Many rocks were removed during the work, including Le Petit Crapaud, so the approaches to our present harbour are a little safer.

The foundation stone of Elizabeth Castle breakwater was laid with great pomp, on 29 August, 1872. The *Acte des Etats* for that date says:

'The States assembled and proceeded to the spot where the stone was to be laid, the Magistrates in their togas and the clergy in their robes, all preceded by the Royal Mace. Detachments of each of the Regiments of the Royal Militia led the way.'

The Bailiff (John Hammond, Esq.) was conducted by the Engineers and Members of the Harbours Committee to the ceremonial platform. The Greffier (Gervaise Le Gros, Esq., later Jurat) read the *Actes des Etats* authorising the work to be done and the Order in Council confirming the same.

The Dean of Jersey, the Very Rev. W. C. Le Breton, M.A. (father of Lillie Langtry) offered a prayer which occupies two thirds pages of folio in the *Actes des Etats*!

The Breakwater was to be 60 feet high and 38 feet in width at the top, in depths of water varying from 12 to 20 feet at low water, ordinary spring tides. At the head upon the Platte Rock

The building of Elizabeth Castle Breakwater about 1876. The crane Hercules with engine, wagons and barge. Had it been built before the arm from Havre des Pas it would have provided the shelter that the arm needed. The entrance to St. Helier harbour would have been where the barge is, or somewhat beyond.

Pier Road: the road to the pier in 1750. When Fort Regent was built on Mont de la Ville in 1806, the spoil was thrown over the road on to the beach with the permission of the Seigneur who owned the foreshore. This is now Commercial Buildings. La Folie Inn is built on the rock, or near to it. In the background right is l'Hermitage, the rock where Helier lived around 550 AD. Elizabeth Castle Breakwater had not been built as it was constructed about seventy years after Fort Regent.
(Photo courtesy of the Harbourmaster).

there would be an Iron Lighthouse 50 feet above the mean tide level. The entrance into the Harbour between the heads of the Breakwater and the Landing Pier would be 830 feet wide.

A glass bottle was then deposited in the cavity prepared for it and was hermetically sealed. It contained various *Actes des Etats*; a plan of the new harbour; a map of Jersey; a box containing English and Jersey money; two medals commemorating the Visit of Queen Victoria and Prince Albert; the Almanac for the current year (*British Times and Jersey Press*); and copies of newspapers.

The *Chroniques* waxed indignant over the whole affair. The pavilion or tent for the use of the Harbours Committee cost £322 and the flowers £127. The plaque 'He bringeth them into their desired haven' should have been in Jersey French. The paper was scandalised because the climax of the day was a sumptuous Dinner at the Royal Yacht Hotel. The Lieutenant Governor and Bailiff were missing. The *Chroniques* reported that when a certain toast was proposed, Jurat de Quetteville called out to Mr. Vickery, one of the Deputies for St. Helier, "Are you ready, Mr. Vickery, are your glasses full"? To which Mr. Vickery replied, "Yes, we are always working" — an indication that the elbow was always lifting.

At the time of the wake at the Royal Yacht Hotel, work at the Pointe de Pas was proceeding apace. Yet within three years enormous gales did many thousands of pounds of damage, and there was a great upheaval in the States. The *Nouvelle Chroniques* published a letter from Captain Saumarés dated 22 November, 1875, deploring the fact that, on the day of destruction of the Works, the Harbours Committee had the *Mauvaise Plaisanterie* to hold a wake at the Pomme d'Dor Hotel.

Two days later there was a row in the States. A hostile opponent was Advocate H. E. Le Vavasseur dit Durell, then Deputy of St. Helier, later Constable of St. Helier, and finally Attorney General. He felt the work should be discontinued. On 11 February, 1876, the House voted to discontinue the work.

The remains of the huge caissons out to sea from Pointe des Pas were still be to seen after the war. They disappeared when the Jersey Electricity Power Station was built on reclaimed land. It was probably the only major scheme stopped midway to completion in the history of the Island, and in spite of an Order-in-Council authorising the work. It was stopped because of the violence of weather and tides.

THE SIGNAL STATION

A SMALL BOY of fourteen applied for a job with Lloyds' of London. He was ordered to appear before the secretary of Lloyds', a man named Hozier of international fame.

He stood in silence in the huge office while the secretary worked on papers. Hozier suddenly looked up, glared at him and snapped, "Where is Galle?"

"Ceylon, Sir", replied the boy.

"Start on Monday," said the great man, and bent over his papers.

After surviving the shortest interview in history — eight words between the two of them — the boy ascended through the ranks and ultimately took Hozier's place. Hozier married, and a daughter named Clementine was born. She married Winston Churchill, and so Hozier became Churchill's father-in-law. He went on to invent Lloyds' signal stations. A huge chain world-wide kept Lloyds' in touch with every ship insured with them, and every owner wanted to be classified as A1 at Lloyds.

The stations were used by ship owners to pass on orders as to where the ship should berth, what cargo to pick up, and so forth. The masters reported coal in hand and state of ship, including sails damage. A station such as the Lizard was sometimes in touch by flag and lights with ten ships. There was no telephone or telegraph in those days.

Gales caused ships to founder, and did great damage. There was no way of transmitting weather forecasts, so ships sailed into the unknown. In 1861, Admiral Fitzroy invented the storm cone, a black triangle to hoist on Lloyds' signal stations. The point downwards indicated a gale expected from the south, and the point upwards, a gale from the north. A gale is force 8 or above on the Beaufort Scale.

The point about the above tale is that Jersey appeared on the first list of stations to receive an order to hoist the storm cone. This was because the telegraph cable had been laid to Jersey in 1858. Although there was no official Lloyds' station, the Island had a signal station from 1708.

The station erected on Mont de la Ville, or Town Hill, now Fort Regent, was one of many. A chain of stations was established not simply to signal ships, as St. Helier was not then a port, but as a defence measure. The signal, 'French man o' war steering for the island,' was enough to turn the Militia out. There was a permanent danger of invasion by the French, and, indeed, they landed in the small hours of 6 January, 1781, at La Rocque. No signals were made because it was pitch dark. The French had good intelligence.

The ten stations, according to M. B. Kavanagh, were: La Moye; Noirmont Point; Le Mont de la Ville (Fort Regent); Herket (Mont Ubé); Verclut; Mont Orgueil; Rozel; La Bouley; Mont Mado; and Grosnez. They were erected on elevated ground and were manned by Naval Personnel, a Lieutenant, a Midshipman, and two seamen. At Grosnez it was said that on a clear day 'it may be discovered that Ships of War are riding at their anchors in Guernsey Roads.' General Don ordered that, in the event of an alarm, the Red Flag be hoisted to the top of the mast, and two black balls be placed at the west yard-arm, and two cannon shots to be fired. A total of 56 signals were used to cover all shipping.

Conditions were not good. The signalman at La Moye sent a letter to Captain Bichard, Harbour Master on 15 October 1883:

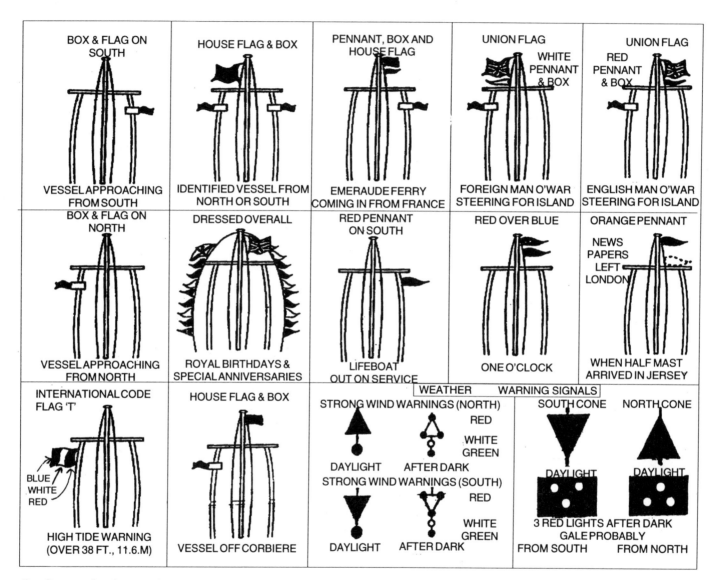

BOX & FLAG ON SOUTH	**HOUSE FLAG & BOX**	**PENNANT, BOX AND HOUSE FLAG**	**UNION FLAG** WHITE PENNANT & BOX	**UNION FLAG** RED PENNANT & BOX
VESSEL APPROACHING FROM SOUTH	IDENTIFIED VESSEL FROM NORTH OR SOUTH	EMERAUDE FERRY COMING IN FROM FRANCE	FOREIGN MAN O'WAR STEERING FOR ISLAND	ENGLISH MAN O'WAR STEERING FOR ISLAND
BOX & FLAG ON NORTH	**DRESSED OVERALL**	**RED PENNANT ON SOUTH**	**RED OVER BLUE**	**ORANGE PENNANT** NEWS PAPERS LEFT LONDON
VESSEL APPROACHING FROM NORTH	ROYAL BIRTHDAYS & SPECIAL ANNIVERSARIES	LIFEBOAT OUT ON SERVICE	ONE O'CLOCK	WHEN HALF MAST ARRIVED IN JERSEY

INTERNATIONAL CODE FLAG 'T'

BLUE
WHITE
RED

HIGH TIDE WARNING (OVER 38 FT., 11.6.M)

HOUSE FLAG & BOX

VESSEL OFF CORBIERE

WEATHER   WARNING SIGNALS

STRONG WIND WARNINGS (NORTH)
RED
WHITE
GREEN
DAYLIGHT   AFTER DARK
STRONG WIND WARNINGS (SOUTH)
RED
WHITE
GREEN
DAYLIGHT   AFTER DARK

SOUTH CONE   NORTH CONE
DAYLIGHT   DAYLIGHT
3 RED LIGHTS AFTER DARK
GALE PROBABLY
FROM SOUTH   FROM NORTH

Fort Regent signals
(By courtesy of R.M. Bullen, Harbourmaster)

Deare Sir – Captain Bishar,
I wish to report the Oreable Condichon the House and
Lookout is at La moye Signal station. Dear Sir, the
Roof of the House is Quite Likey and the toyles are all
Lussen with the North and South and West Gailles and
Winds, and so all the shutters and window Freames and
doors are Qite totten. The House is so old … Deare Sir
there is no supply of water and no convinces … The
House is so far Inland that I am Obliged to walk from
three to four hundred yards to the Point to take the
vessels and flags in all kinds of weather, so I am allway
catching heavy colds ….
Dear Sir the man that i Rerled, Mr. Ranney dide thow a
sevrier cold and the man Before him Mr Corros went
blind all so a nother man Life was Lost thro this Place".
Deare Sir, I must Conclude,
I remain your humble and oligent Servant,

Pensioner BENJAMIN DAVIES
St Brealades
St Hiliers, Jersey.
Vraie Copie des Roles W. Bertram Godfray, Greffier.

The matter was referred to the Lt. Governor of Jersey,
Major General Henry Wray, who passed it to the Commanding
Officer, Royal Engineers. On 8 June, 1885, it went to the
Lords Commissioners of the Admiralty.

The storm cone was known as the Board of Trade warning
signal, and was known here as the 'dread signal.' A telegram
ordering its hoisting was received by the Harbour Master, and
another telegram ordered it to be lowered when the danger
was past. It was always reported in the *Jersey Evening Post*.
After the war, with Jersey becoming a yachting centre, a ball
was added to the cone if a wind of force 6 or 7 was expected.

This is because many small boats find such winds dangerous,
especially when the tides are huge. A triangle of three red
lights is the night signal for the cone, and the triangle plus a
white and green light for the cone and ball.

The mast and wind vane – surely the most exposed in the
Island – is 100 feet high, and the yard arm runs north to south.
All ships from the direction of Guernsey are signalled on the
north yard arm, and those from France on the south. The
house flag goes to the masthead. Before the advent of steam,
a ball under the yard arm meant 'a sail in sight.' When steam
came, a box and red flag under the yard arm meant 'a steamer
in sight.'

In the old days the single pennant under the yard arm
meant 'mail arrived in Guernsey' and two pennants meant 'mail
left Guernsey.' A box added showed that it had been sighted
by the keepers of Corbière Lighthouse, and it was flagged when
it passed the lighthouse. Everybody watched for the signal
because the boat carried the mail and the previous day's newspapers.

It was noticed after the war by those going off night duty at
the Airport, that boys and girls were crowding outside
newsagents waiting for the papers in order to deliver them
before school. But it was known that the paper 'plane had not
left London. So an orange pennant now appears at the masthead to indicate that the aircraft has left London, and when at
half mast, the newspapers have arrived. As it is normally here
at sunrise or before, the signal seldom flies, but when the
papers are late it is very helpful, and is looked for by many who
are involved with newspaper delivery. No aircraft in the world
is flagged except in Jersey on Fort Regent.

A red pennant shows that the lifeboat is out, and the letter
'T' in the international code, is flown when a spring tide of 38
feet or more is running.

The signalman is responsible to the Principal Meteorological
Officer for the sunshine recorder, so crucial to the Island. It is

situated next to the signal post.

From very early days, two pennants, red over blue, signalled, 'it is 8 or 1 o'clock.' This was a crucial signal in the days before Big Ben and the time signal. Employers shut the gate as the pennants went up and late workers were locked out. The signal was lowered at 8.05 a.m. and 1.05 p.m. Today, only the one o'clock signal is flown.

Because Jersey is west of Greenwich, which is longitude 0 degrees, the Island used Jersey Legal Time which was 8 minutes 28 seconds after Greenwich. So when the clocks at Greenwich struck midday, Jersey clocks said 1151 and 32 seconds.

Longitude is 15 degrees to the hour. So if Jersey was 15 degrees west of Greenwich our clocks would be one hour behind Greenwich. New York is five hours back. If Jersey was 15 degrees east of Greenwich, the clocks would be one hour ahead of Greenwich.

As it is, Jersey is Latitude 49° north, Longitude 2° 07 seconds west – hence 8 minutes 28 seconds after Greenwich.

On 11 June, 1898, the States abolished Jersey Legal Time, and ordered Greenwich Mean Time to be used.

The chimes of Big Ben don't count. Correct time is the first stroke of the hour. With the pips, it is the beginning of the sound of the last pip that is correct time. Before wireless, Signalman Touzel, an old Naval sea dog, went by the strike of the Town Church clock. Incidentally, it fell to Touzel to hoist the Swastika in 1940. The Germans arrived with photographers. 'I made sure I turned my back on them as I did so,' he said in disgust.

A pre-war photograph of Fort Regent Signal Station. The mast is 100 feet high and the yard-arm runs north/south. The north cone is flying on the north inner halyard, and the pennant at the masthead shows that the mailboat has arrived. It is lowered to half-mast when the mail reaches the post office, and remains so for two hours while the mail is sorted.

THE GREAT DROUGHT OF 1975-76

ON 1 JUNE 1975 a northerly airstream brought snow as far south as London. Within 72 hours the shivering country was drawing in air from the African deserts and the temperature soared up to the 80s in a dramatic about turn. This was the herald of a drought which was to last until September 1976.

The entry of the fair maiden called Summer 1975 was thrilling, and there followed long days of brilliant sunshine — June alone had 356 hours. There was lush grass and abundant foliage after a rather wet spring. Flowers were in profusion, and brooks and streams gurgled contentedly to the sea. Yachts drifted in lights airs under sun, moon and stars. The teeth of Time gnawed Summer away and Autumn came in with stealth, showing no sign of a change of type. Only November was at all wet.

The winter and spring which followed were unusually dry, and great concern began to be felt. Depressions which came roaring in from the Atlantic were diverted northwards, only skirting the west and north-west coasts of Britain. The winter Continental blocking 'high' caused anti-cyclonic gloom, with the result that only 43 hours of bright sunshine were recorded in December, an average of 1.4 hours per day, compared with nearly 12 hours per day in June. Only a little over an inch of rain fell during the month.

As the Spring progressed so the Azores anti-cyclone took over to keep the depressions on a more northerly track than usual. Cirrus clouds, which normally speak of rain to come, were false witnesses. Average barometric pressure exceeded 30 inches (1015.9 millibars) month by month. The ridge of high pressure took root in the South-West Approaches, and had the effect of either diverting rain-belts or weakening them; fronts tended to die out as soon as they began to cross the country. A remarkable feature was the almost entire absence of thunderstorms in spite of the exceptionally high temperatures. Even when the barometer was relatively low it failed to rain, as the air was dry up to very high levels. But the dominant feature was the rather high and uniform barometer readings (see upper figure overleaf). There were no violent changes; the pressure tended to sink rather than fall, and then it came back into the same basic situation. All this was reversed after the end of the drought in September 1976. Then there were gales, rain, floods, thunderstorms and violent changes of barometric pressure (see lower figure overleaf).

It is interesting to note that the potato crop did remarkably well in spite of the fact that only 1.4 inches of rain (34.6 millimetres) fell between 1 April and 31 August 1976. The roots got down to such moisture as there was. The potato has always been said to be a near tropical plant, and so it proved to be. The crop was on the light side, but prices were high, and it was harvested in great clouds of dust. Numerous furze and heath fires, together with harvesters, caused a pall of smoke and dust to hang over the island. Strong winds filled the roads and lanes with dust, and soil erosion became a real problem.

We can properly speak of the fair maiden called Summer 1975, but Summer 1976 was a withered shrew. The island was a barren desert, unbelievably different from that of 1975. Emaciated cows dragged themselves round dusty fields devoid of grass, milk production fell by 16% at the height of the visitor season, and cattle were on winter feed in searing sunshine. Temperatures in the 80s and 90s were commonplace throughout the summer months. For 15 consecutive days between 23rd June and 7 July the temperature reached, or exceeded 90°F (32°C) at some place in the British Isles, which is a

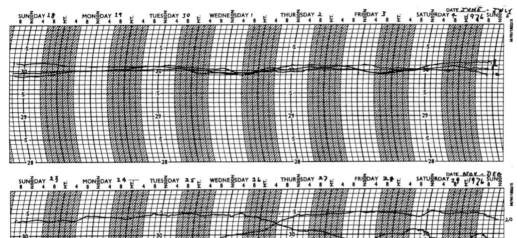

Barograph charts for three consecutive weeks superimposed, of atmospheric pressure recorded at St. John's Rectory.

Above: 28 June to 19 July 1976: Note the continuous steady and fairly high pressure; this was at the height of the drought and heat wave with air temperatures up to 92°F (32°C).

Below: 23 November to 13 December 1976. Note the variations between very low and very high pressure; during this period violent gales and heavy rain occurred.

record. The highest in June was 96°F (35.6°C) at Southampton. No rain at all was recorded at some Jersey stations in June, nor for the first 29 days of August.

The enormous influx of visitors coincided with the highest temperatures and evaporation rates. Official orders were given banning the filling of swimming pools, watering of gardens and washing of cars. Everyone co-operated willingly, but life was tinged with apprehension. The planting of cauliflowers was, for some, a disaster. Many plants stood up for three days and then withered away. Water-carriers careered around the island by day and by night, and bore-holes were sunk by the dozen in a desperate search for water.

The consumption of water exceeded the inflow into the reservoirs from the beginning of the year, and the desalination plant at La Rosière — the only one in working condition in the British Isles — ran from May to October, and prevented a

desperate situation from becoming dangerous. By the end of August, when seven inches of rain had fallen in eight months, the reservoirs were at such a low level that it was obvious that the island would have been completely without water very shortly but for the desalination plant. Wells which had never failed in living memory were drying out, possibly due to the excessive numbers of new bore holes, and intensive irrigation methods. Among streams and brooks which dried up late in 1975 or early in 1976, noted by Dr Frank Le Maistre, were:

1 Le Dou du Gris Pais and Le Dou de la Brecquette: both fed by Le Dou ou Canné des Vaux with its source at La Fontaine, Millais; never known to stop running previously.
2 Le Dou de la Saline: the source is at Le Marais.
3 Le Canné des Vaux Cuisson: has its source north of St. Ouen's Church and the old Perquage; dry by January 1976.

4 Le Canné ou Dou des Vaux de Carteret: south of St. Ouen's Church running into La Mare au Seigneur; dry by summer 1976.

5 Le Dou Fondan: below the Airport, down Le Mont Fondan; never before dried up, but did in summer 1976.

6 Le Dou de la Pulente: dry by summer 1976; never dry before.

7 Le Canné des Vaux Doux: into Petit Port; dry by summer 1976.

The above is a selection from the 25 brooks and streams which normally flow into Les Mielles – St Ouen's Bay – and which failed. La Mare au Seigneur – St Ouen's Pond – has not been so low since the Great Drought of 1834 (L'année d'La Grand' S'crêche) when a St Ouennais named Vibert walked from the east verge to La Motte in the centre.

The numbers of open-land fires increased from an average of 125 per annum to 329 in 1976. Mr W. G. Mahoney, the Chief Fire Officer, said that the countryside was ready to explode. One of the worst fires was on L'Ouaisné Common, where tankers brought effluent from Bellozanne Works for fire-fighting purposes owing to the lack of water.

By the middle of September 1976 only seven inches of rain had fallen, and it seemed certain that the record dry year of 1921 with 16.77 inches would be toppled. But there arose a little cloud out of the sea shaped like a man's hand, as in the days of Elijah, and the deluge followed. Between then and the end of December no less than 20 inches of rain fell. That is a rate in excess of 60 inches a year. The Fire Service was then working against water rather than without it.

The effect upon the island was rather like that of a small child putting water on a painting book with a brush – the colours suddenly appear. Hearts were filled with gladness as the island was transformed by the refreshing sound and regenerative power of water. But it was a long, long time before all the wells came back into use – some were dry until after Christmas – and not all things revived.

One inch is approximately 25 millimetres. Annual average rainfall in Jersey is 825 mm (33 ins). One inch of rain equals 100 tons of water per acre (2.25 vergées). The three months period of June, July and August 1976 was the driest ever recorded

The calendar years of 1975 and 1976 are not particularly distinguished by their rainfall totals of 28.54 and 26.76 inches respectively – against an average annual of 33 inches – because 1975 had a wet spring and 1976 had a wet autumn. But the period 1 October 1975 to 30 September 1976 produced 16.9 inches. The real record was 0.4 inches (11.1 mm) in June, July and August 1976. There are no 92 consecutive days in our meteorological records to equal that.

The years 1911 and 1921 were hot and dry and the shortage of water was grievous to bear. The years 1971-76 all had rainfall below the average of 33 inches except 1974, and the summer of 1976 was considered by the British Meteorological Office to be unprecedented in 250 years. We may properly go back to the year of the Battle of Jersey, 1781, and note that Gilbert White wrote in that year: The upland villages are in great distress for want of water; men sow their wheat in absolute dust .... My well sinks and is very low ... the well at Old Place in the Parish of East Tisted, though 270 feet, will not afford water for brewing ....'

It is just about true to say that no public event, such as an agricultural show, fête or bazaar had to be cancelled because of rain at any time during the summers of 1975 or 1976. The children did not have a single complete wet day during their summer holidays, and they will surely grow up to talk of the brilliant hot summers of their childhood. We have lived through meteorological history: the records may stand for centuries.

Skating on St. Ouen's Pond (La Mare au Seigneur) on 23 January 1963.
(Photo Jersey Evening Post).

St. Aubin's Harbour frozen,
22 January 1963.
(Photo Jersey Evening Post).

SNOW

SNOW IS COMPARATIVELY RARE in Jersey because we are kept relatively warm by the surrounding sea. Thus a west or south-west wind is mild, but an easterly wind off the Continent is cold and dry in winter.

In this century the heaviest snowfall occurred during the night of 11-12 February, 1929, when a blizzard came in. Both the railways from the Weighbridge to La Corbière, and the line from Snow Hill to Gorey Pier, were unable to operate, but the report said, 'gangs of men are out clearing the lines.' Children walked to school over hedges, as roads were full of drifts. Most children went to the parish school, and as there was no radio, and virtually no telephone to convey messages, the whole of Europe and Britain were crippled by the severest Arctic blast for years. The temperature in Warsaw fell to its lowest point for 105 years.

Members of the States normally came in by train, and the sitting started at 10.15 a.m. because the train got in at 10 a.m. Only 16 members made it to town that day, so the sitting was abandoned as there was no quorum. Deputy E. B. Renouf suggested that "for the benefit of future generations, and for meteorologists in particular, the Greffier should make a special Act of the States recording the fact." No such Act has been necessary since.

The funeral of Mr. Y. Campbell Goldsmid had to be postponed because it was impossible to get the hearse up to Almorah Cemetry, and the Shell Motor lorry was the first vehicle of any description to reach l'Etacq, having 'pushed its way bodily' through deep drifts. Drifts of seven feet were reported in St. Saviour, while in St. Brelade, according to 'a well-known resident of La Moye,' the edge of the sea was frozen. In Trinity it was the same story with byroads and lanes

impassable to anything but sleighs. The whole of Europe and Britain was crippled by the severest Arctic blast for years. The temperature in Warsaw fell to its lowest point for 105 years.

The winter of 1939-40 was cold. Members of the Royal Militia Island of Jersey, on guard at Plémont because of the telephone cable to England, noted that the waterfall from the top of Plémont to the caves froze into one long icicle. Those on guard at the Airport were in agony as they were marched out to the end of the airfield in the east wind at 2 a.m.

But 1946-47 was colder, with reservoirs frozen, and there was a mass of frozen pipes bursting in houses because lagging on any scale was unknown. There was some hardship because food was still rationed, and the Island had still not got over the Occupation.

The short sea track from St. Malo and Carteret to Jersey means that warm air from the Continent in summer is not modified as much as it is modified in Guernsey which is further out in the Channel — and Alderney more so. So Jersey tends to be warmer than Guernsey in summer, but colder than Guernsey in winter. The relatively high sea temperature in winter causes Guernsey to be warmer because of the longer sea track. Jersey faces the sun — the cliffs are in the north and the beaches in the south. Guernsey is the opposite with a gentle slope to the north. Therefore Jersey tends to grow things out of doors, while Guernsey concentrates on greenhouses, their grapes being famous years ago, and tomatoes equally so, until the advent of the European Community.

In Jersey, snow lies on the ground at 9 a.m. for three days a year on average. It is possible to go for ten years without much more than a few snow showers, and then have a month of snow as in 1929 and 1962-63.

Left: Snow Hill, St. Helier, 1 February 1963. The building on the left was the terminus of the Jersey Eastern Railway which ran to Gorey Pier and which closed on 21 June 1929. On the right is the Eastern Hotel ... one could buy a ticket to Paris at the station – Snow Hill to Gorey Pier; Gorey Pier to Carteret; Carteret to Paris.

Right: La Frouquie rock, 700 yards beyond La Corbière Lighthouse, on which the St. Malo was holed in April 1995 (see pages 43-44). (Photo courtesy David Fry)

DAY THE GAS FAILED

THE WETTEST DAY in the hundred-year history of Maison St. Louis Observatory, noted by Mark Le Cornu, was Monday, 24 August, 1931. This was in the school summer holidays, and at the height of the visitor season.

A depression over Brittany – rare in August – caused a severe north-east gale, and heavy rain. There was considerable anxiety when the Southern and Great Western mailboats sailed into terrific seas, and nobody knew if they had reached their destinations. It provoked a leading article in the *Jersey Evening Post* asking why no information was given by the companies concerned 'in view of the new invention of wireless.'

The *St. Julien* (Captain Richardson) failed to enter Weymouth Harbour, and had to go astern after two attempts. It sought shelter in Portland Naval Harbour for only the second time in 43 years. She was there all night, and the boat train did not arrive at Paddington until noon on the following day. The *St. Patrick* (Captain Sanderson) with 224 passengers arrived at St. Helier Harbour at 1 p.m. instead of 9.15 a.m. The *ss Lorina* encountered mountainous seas off the Casquets, and was slightly damaged. The *Isle of Jersey* (Captain Holt) made good time. The passengers looked squeamish, but one man came down the gangway wearing a straw hat and carrying a tennis racket. A yacht belonging to Mr. E. F. Rive was sunk and buried in the sand of St. Aubin's Harbour, and a new hydroplane, *Miss Happy*, belonging to Mr. Dobbs of St. Aubin, was swamped and damaged. Other yachts in the Channel Islands area were missing. Trees were brought down and telephone lines damaged. Mr. J. R. Stanhope of the Telephone Department said that telephonic communication with England was interrupted. A pony in some stables in Victoria Road had a narrow escape when it was rescued when the water had reached its stomach, but a number of fowls were drowned. Water in Plat Douet Road was three feet deep, and at Maufant it was four feet. The Recreation Grounds at Greve d'Azette, and the F.B. Fields (opened three years earlier) were under water and unserviceable to the disgust of those who turned up with tennis rackets and golf clubs the next day. The cottages at Old Bagot Manor suffered from flood water, as did the cottages at La Rocque Wesleyan Chapel. Clothing was saturated.

At Beghin's in King Street, work was in hand with the drains. As a result the shop was flooded, and hundreds of pairs of boots and shoes in the stock room were ruined. Water entered the ground floor of the Lily White Laundry, and the cottages near Bagot Laundry. Town Mills was one of the worst spots because the brook under Trinity Hill overflowed its banks and caused a wall to collapse. Water flooded in ground floors of Old Tan Yard, Le Geyt Road and Grands Vaux. A woman who fled 400 yards through water saw one of her stockings in the gutter, and, further on, a sock. There was a landslide at L'Hermitage, St. Saviour.

The situation at the Gas Works was really serious, and the manager, Mr. Harry Morris, was called out. He ordered all fires to be drawn owing to the risk of an explosion. All gas was cut off. Mr. Morris said it was impossible to say when the service would be restored as he could not estimate the damage until the Fire Service had pumped the water out. 'The Constable of St. Helier presents his compliments to the Tradesmen of the Island and requests those who have electric light to keep their lights on tonight and until the gas lamps can again be lighted. Those on street corners are particularly requested to do this.' – so ran a notice in the *Evening Post*.

The tradesmen loyally responded to Constable Ferguson's request, and kept electricity on for the two nights that there was no gas.

RAIN AND FLOODS

AT THE END OF JANUARY, 1978, the wallflowers and daffodils were already out and the birds were singing as in January, 1995. Spring could not be far behind. However, the barometer was rising over Hudson Bay, Canada, to 31 inches, and falling off North Carolina's Cape Hateras to 29 inches. So began a chain reaction which showed up winter at its most savage. A storm of hurricane proportions moved up the Ohio Valley and the east coast of the United States with the accompanying blizzard virtually obliterating New York. After that, the pressure rose over Greenland and linked across northern latitudes to the Siberian 'high' which had moved north of Moscow and ridging across Scandinavia. This led to a horrifying blizzard over Scotland.

The stage was set for the worst combination of winter weather possible — high pressure from Canada to Siberia, and low from north of the Azores to the Mediterranean. That is the opposite of the traditional pattern of high over the Azores and low over Iceland, so the wind had to be basically easterly rather than westerly. The east coast of Britain was selected for the next brutal attack, and the whole area vanished under snow. The high over England slackened, and a vast depression of 956 millibars, 28.1 inches, north of the Azores, sent warm moist air racing towards south-west England. Bracknell Weather Centre forecast that it would spread across the whole country, thus ending the cold spell, and south-west England grinned contentedly to itself having got away with it again as usual. But things went wrong.

The moment the rain reached the Isles of Scilly, the anti-cyclone of 1056 millibars, 31.2 inches, over Greenland sent a ridge of high pressure down towards Britain like a giant fist. It stopped the warm air in its tracks after it had reached the Isle of Wight, and flung it back and left it lurking off Brest and the Channel Islands. Jersey was on a knife-edge, balanced between warm and cold air masses. It had neither rain nor snow in its truest sense, and it was required to settle for freezing rain. It even had ice needles. Freezing rain is caused by warm air from the Atlantic coming over the top. Because warm air is lighter than cold, it lifted over the freezing ground. If anyone had gone up in a balloon he or she would have found that the temperature actually increased with height.

Thus the precipitation fell as rain because the temperature at cloud level was far above freezing. But the moment it hit the trees and the ground which were below freezing, the water froze, and all things were weighed down by ice. Incidentally, freezing rain was the thing most dreaded by air pilots in the old days. Ice accretion has brought many aircraft crashing to the ground, just as it has sunk ships off Iceland and elsewhere by its sheer weight. To this day, when the shipping forecast mentions south-east Iceland it ends in winter with the words 'light — or moderate or severe — icing.'

People witnessed the dramatic effect of this in the form of branches glowing with ice, being bowed to the ground, the whole trees crashing about their ears. The cruelty was the strength of the wind which ruthlessly shook trees groaning under the weight of ice. The night was rudely disturbed by the tinkling of ice crashing to the ground rather like a burglar smashing a window. Jersey had never had experience of such things. All this occurred on the high ground of the Island — St. John, Trinity and St. Martin where the temperature is always a degree or so lower than St. Helier. At sea level the ground was not frozen, so the rain leaving the clouds arrived as rain on the ground and on the trees. Dr. Frank Le Maistre at l'Etacq, recorded 63 millimetres of rain, or 2.5 inches, on Sunday morning, 20 February, 1978. "In all my 46 years and over of recording rainfall at St.Ouen and elsewhere, I have never had a recording like that at La Brecquette," he said.

So the drama of freezing rain and trees blocking roads was eclipsed by rain which didn't freeze. Floods at Gorey Village left 50 people homeless. Young Richard and Catherine Lake used a rowing boat to rescue people in the main street of Gorey Village. Gorey Marsh was a sheet of water caused by the stream from Queen's Valley to Gorey Village slip overflowing. Elderly people at Les Houmets Home were evacuated through a ground floor window to a tractor and trailer. Electricity was cut off in several areas, and telephone lines came down. In all, there were floods, fog, freezing rain and gales. St. Peter's Valley and the Recreation Grounds at Grève d'Azette were badly flooded.

Had the Island been all high ground, the loss of trees would have been as great as in the storm of 1987. But they would have been brought down by ice rather than wind. Had the storm occurred on 20 January instead of 20 February, the temperature would have been a couple of degrees lower and the whole Island would have had two feet of snow – greater than that of February, 1929. South-west England had the worst snow for years.

We are always hearing of snow on the mountains of Scotland and the hills and moors of England. But even in Jersey the high ground can make a difference when the temperature is in the crucial area of a degree above or below freezing. Generally in the lower layers temperature falls off at 5.4° F per 1,000 feet so that even at 200 feet elevation there will be a drop of one degree.

In all this, no life was lost and nobody was injured. But it was arguably the most dramatic day's weather this century because of the great variation. It is unlikely to occur again for a very long time.

David Le Feuvre, seated, with Alfred Marks, groundsman of the Recreation Grounds, Grève d'Azette, 31 January 1961. (Photo Jersey Evening Post).

61

ANTARCTICA

THE SUMMER IN the Continent of Antarctica is in January, and the sensation in January, 1995, was the breaking away of an iceberg in the Weddell Sea. This particular berg was larger than the Isle of Wight, so it was a rare find. In the old days, explorers landing on a berg that size would not know that it had broken away because the distance would be too great, but aircraft surveys and satellites have revealed all things.

The regional climate has warmed by 2.5°C since the 1940's — which is a lot — and there is much speculation that global warming has started, but it is a region and not the globe. But things are by no means easy to interpret.

Icebergs have always been breaking away. There were great numbers around Cape Horn in 1855, and more than usual in the 1920s and 30s. Bergs from the north polar ice cap broke into the north Atlantic and were not seriously monitored until the White Star liner *Titanic* hit one on its maiden voyage and sank with the loss of more than 1,400 lives in 1912.

Further news of Antarctica in the summer of 1995 came with the discovery that it was possible to sail round James Ross Island at the northern tip of the Antarctica Peninsula around 1,500 miles from the South Pole. That had never been known before. It will, of course, freeze over in their autumn. The trouble is that if the temperature rises and water appears where there should be ice, more moisture is picked up and more snow falls. That tends to lower the temperature and the ice comes back. It is a self-correcting mechanism.

It is said that the ice shelves in Antarctica shed 2,020,000,000,000 tons of ice and snow each year, and gain a similar amount from snowfall on the Continent.

These huge snowfields, covering a substantial part of the earth, govern the weather of the world. Without them and their cold air meeting warm tropical air, depressions would not form, and rainfall would vanish away. If it all melted, the world sea level would rise enormously. Even if the ice on Greenland alone melted, it would have an effect on the sea. The ice cap is 8,000 feet thick, which means one would have to dig a hole 8,000 feet deep to reach soil. It would probably be below sea level.

What happens in the Arctic and Antarctic affects Jersey weather and the level of the sea in the long run. Not in the lifetime of any person, but in thousands of years.

St. Aubin's School, 25 January 1958.
(Photo Jersey Evening Post).

JERSEY TIDES

ALMOST THE ONLY THING taught about the tides is that high water occurs one hour later every day, and that it takes six hours to come in and six hours to go out. That is not true. A neap tide can be two hours later than the previous day's tide, and a spring tide can be half an hour later than the previous day. That means that spring tides take less than six hours to come in, and neap tides more.

A peak spring tide rises 40 feet, 12.2 metres, above the line (0) or datum on Victoria Pier, while a weak neap tide rises 24 feet above datum. But the catch is that a neap tide only drops to 16 feet above datum, thus giving a vertical rise of only 8 feet. Thus there are no savage currents with a neap, and no possibility of being cut off because it rises at an average of only 18 inches per hour.

A high water of 40 feet means that if you put a stone at low water it will be under 40 feet of water at high water. On a flat beach it can come in 3 miles, but at the harbour the water will rise 40 feet up the wall.

The highest of the spring tides is the third tide after the new and full moon — about two days — and the weakest of the neap tides is two days after the first and last quarters of the moon when there is half a moon in the sky. The full moon rises at sunset and sets at sunrise.

The peak spring is high around 7.30 a.m. and 7.30 p.m. G.M.T., and the weakest neap is high at lunch time and around midnight G.M.T. From this we can deduce that nobody is likely to be cut off in the morning when the tide is rising and high at lunch time, because it is either a neap or an ebbing spring. The danger is in the afternoon between 3 p.m. and 6 p.m. when the spring tide is flowing.

Children love seeing the waves breaking over the wall in St. Aubin's and elsewhere, but have they ever noticed, or been told, that it never occurs at lunchtime — always between 6 a.m. and 9 a.m. and 6 p.m. and 9 p.m.?

The tide does not ebb and flow at a uniform rate. It is rather like a car starting with the accelerator well down until the fourth hour when it coasts gradually to a halt.

If we take a spring tide with a vertical rise of 36 feet (which means one of 38 feet dropping to 2 feet above datum) we need to divide it into 12 parts. It rises one-twelfth in the first hour which is 3 feet, two-twelfths in the second hour which is 6 feet, and so on. The chart looks like this:

Hours	Twelfths	Feet
1	1	3
2	2	6
3	3	9
4	3	9
5	2	6
6	1	3

From that chart we see that it comes in 18 feet during the third and fourth hours — half its distance. So, Auntie Ethel, settling in her deck chair with the tide well down, can be swamped if she dozes. It also means that the greatest danger of being cut off is between 3 p.m. and 6 p.m. because low water on a spring tide is around 2 p.m. G.M.T. It is then — with a spring — that currents are at their peak. It comes in at 9 feet an hour at its strongest, compared with 18 inches per hour with a neap.

La Rocco Tower, St. Ouen's Bay, was built between 1796 and 1801 as part of the defences against Napoleon. Note the shapely walls and the size of the people and the boat. Before the war the States let the tower out to Lady Houston, an eccentric who had a yacht with the words 'Wake up England' in huge letters which were illuminated at night when anchored in the Solent. She was often seen wandering about the deck in pink pyjamas, a scandal in those days.

One day a man called on her in Jersey and asked for £100,000. He left with a flea in his ear. The next day her chauffeur delivered a cheque for the full amount. It was not even in an envelope. The man, R.J. Mitchell, went on to develop the Spitfire, which, arguably, saved Britain and the Free World.
(Photo Dr. Frank Le Maistre, O.B.E.)

La Rocco Tower was damaged by German gunfire during the Occupation. The sea destroyed the walls. It was repaired in 1968 by Ronez, but the walls were rounded.
(Photo Jersey Tourism)

THE EQUINOX

The highest spring tides occur in March and September when the sun is vertical to the Equator — hence equinoctial spring tides — and the months either side of them. As high spring tides are followed by a weak spring tide, we get a high once a month. One in February, March and April, and one in August, September and October. A high spring is 40 feet and a weak spring is 33 feet.

The weak spring tides are in November, December and January when the sun is vertical to the Tropic of Capricorn in December, and in May, June and July when the sun is vertical to the Tropic of Cancer. The Mean High Water of Ordnance Survey is 11.1 + 8.1 divided by 2 = 9.6 metres.

The tide comes in from the west Channel and hits the Cherbourg or Cotentin Peninsula where the water is diverted right into the Bay of St. Malo. There it is trapped at Mont St. Michel, and we get an uphill situation. Guernsey has a lesser vertical rise than Jersey, but Chausey Island has a greater rise, while Mont St. Michel is the peak with 46 feet. The highest in the world is that in the Bay of Fundy, Nova Scotia, with 53 feet. It is a restricted area leading to a river rather like the famous Severn Bore which beats Jersey. But we are in Division 1 on a world scale. We should understand and enjoy it.

It is wonderful sitting on the beach at St. Tropez in the Mediterranean, but where is the tide? It hardly moves. Our water moves out through the Alderney Race. Throw a matchbox into the water and it will travel up to 15 miles in an hour. Our sailors, fishermen and yachtsmen need to be expert. One marvels that there are not more tragedies because there are no other places which experience such currents.

Those who don't have a tide table handy should be able to calculate high water within an hour by glancing at the moon. If it is full or new, high water will be around 6 a.m. and 6 p.m. — remember that the peak spring tide is at 7.30 two days later. If there is half a moon in the sky, first and last quarters, then it is a neap tide high around noon and midnight. The moon governs the tides, and it also has an effect on the growth of crops. The tide tables are based on an assumed barometric pressure of 1012 millibars, 29.9 inches (the world average pressure) and no wind. If the barometer is one inch higher at 30.9 , the sea will be one foot lower because the air is pressing it down more. If the pressure is 28.9, the sea will be one foot higher than predicted because the air is not pressing down so much. You therefore get a hump in a depression. But with high pressure and an easterly wind, the sea could be two or three feet lower than expected. In simple language, a tide of 40 feet/ 12.2 metres on a calm day with high pressure will reach the wall. But with low pressure and a gale, it will reach the Town Hall.

For those excited at the prospect of a tide of 40 feet going down to zero, it has to be said that they cannot lose. Low pressure and a gale will bring in huge waves and flooding. But if it is calm with high pressure it will go out further than predicted, perhaps to −2 feet, and be brilliant for low water fishermen.

The Coriolis Force concerning the rotation of the earth means that if you stand with your back to the sea as it enters a river, the water will be higher on the right bank than on the left. If you stand with your back to the river as the water flows out, it will higher on the right bank (the other bank) than on the left. So that right bank has a higher low water and a lower high water. If you stand with your back to the west Channel as the tide comes in, the water will be higher on the French side than on the English side. Thus Jersey has a tide of 40 feet while Weymouth has 8 feet. This Coriolis acceleration greatly complicates things when the tide comes in from the east Channel and gives the Isle of Wight four tides in 24 hours instead of two.

Nobody has ever mastered the subject fully because of the variations of temperature, currents and geographical features.

THE SEA MARK

There is a short iron pole embedded in the rock in all major bays in the Island. It is situated at half tide, or just above, and when it is covered nobody is allowed to remove *vraic* (seaweed) from the beach. This is by law, and the law is enforced to this day.

It is for the comfort of those bathing or sitting on the beaches of the Island. It may not generally be realised that many men made their living by collecting seaweed. Horses and carts were seen by the hundred, especially in the autumn and winter, but nobody dare collect it when the mark was covered. Those who cheated were taken to Court, or dealt with by a punch-up.

Small heaps were allowed to be made from the line of *vraic* at high water even if the mark was covered, but it was not allowed to be removed. Nobody stole another man's heaps. Oddly enough, all this kept the beaches clean. Today, contractors remove the *vraic*.

All the slipways were built of rugged granite in order to help horses to get a grip. A full load of wet seaweed was very heavy to drag up the slope. Water troughs were built on hills such as La Pulente because horses and carts came from all parts of the Island to where the harvest of vraic was greatest. That depended on the wind.

The seaweed was laid out on the sand dunes to dry, and then stacked in lines for sale to those farmers who did not collect individually. It was a very big trade indeed, and it is tragic today to see much of the harvest go to waste for some dreadful fertilizer that affects our water supply. In the old days there was nothing but seaweed. It was part of life.

One thing is maintained for certain by Islanders. The Jersey Royal potato has a far better flavour when grown in a field fertilized by seaweed.

Because of this we should venture to low water on a high spring tide. The area below Seymour Tower is a world apart.

Few people in the Island know what it is like going down to low water mark when it is three miles away from the coast. Few people know that at such times the area of dry land at the Minquiers is larger than Jersey, and that 7,000 years ago that was the high water mark.

A distressing number of people, especially visitors, get cut off by the tide. Those visiting low water spring tide should be taught that the tide will only come in one twelfth of its total distance in the first hour after low water. With a tide of 36 feet, that is 3 feet. So one hour must be the limit. The safe advice is to come back after 30 minutes. Then the tide will have risen by 18 inches. So go right back to the coast because the tide can cut you off a mile from where you are. Remember that people who have never seen the sea know nothing of these things. And those who live on the mainland coast have never experienced tides like we have in Jersey. It is the spring tides that need watching, not the neap.

The Sea Mark at Petit Port, La Corbière: When the iron bar is covered it is forbidden by law to collect seaweed from the beach. This is to avoid disturbing bathers and those enjoying the beach. (Photo May Manton)

66

The narrow entrance to St. Helier Harbour in the 1880s. Steam was new. Fort Regent and Commercial buildings are in the background. The figures 14, 16 and 18 indicate the depth of water in feet. It is low water. A sailing vessel beside the New North Quay has a bucket at the masthead. It is asking for water. This pierhead collapsed in 1889.

St. Aubin's Harbour, 1890. It was the chief port before 1750. A weak neap tide fails to enter the harbour. A ship just missing the spring would have to wait up to ten days to get in. St. Aubin's Terminus of the railway is centre background. It is now St. Brelade's Parish Hall. The curve from the terminus to the tunnel when the line was extended to Corbière was the most severe known on any railway in Europe.

THE GREAT TIDE OF 1967

AT SIXTEEN MINUTES after midnight on the morning of Thursday, 2 November, 1967, it was low water — 2.7 feet above datum. The 'hard' in St. Helier's Harbour was dry, Elizabeth Castle was well above the low-water mark, and the sea was out of sight at La Rocque. The barometer was falling rapidly as a very deep depression of 968 millibars (28.6 inches) over the south Irish Sea moved slowly east. There was thick darkness, no moon, and a south-west gale, when the flood tide came in from the west.

High water was at 5.59 a.m., 38.7 feet above datum. By that time huge ponderous waves were rearing out of the dawn and rushing upon the sea defences with enormous powers and weight. The tops of spent waves flicked stones out of the top of the Esplanade wall as if they were bread-crumbs, and littered them over the road. Mobile cranes were used to move them. The sea rushed past the General Hospital, up Sand Street and Seale Street (Seale Street was named after a former Dean) and flooded the Police cells at the Town Hall.

A Mr. H. W. Carrel, of 5, Belmont Road, wrote: 'The wind rattled the window most of the night, in spite of wedges. At 5 a.m. I shone my torch on the barometer and saw that it had fallen still further, so I dressed hurriedly and went out into the storm, noting by the Flag over Le Gallais' that the wind was south-west. At the Harbour the sea was an absolute fury, huge waves blotting out the street lights. By 5.20 a.m. the sea was half-way up Sand Street and Payn Street, in spite of sand bags. I called at the Police Station and warned them to wake people up. Then the sand-bags gave way and the water went up Dumaresq Street. That was 5.40 a.m. A remarkable thing was that the water was still rising at 6.40 a.m.'

The line of seaweed marking high water was strung along the middle of the Lower Park. The Havre des Pas area suffered greatly, with La Collette Walk blocked by boulders and stones. The Carlton Hotel and the bridge to the bathing pool were damaged, and the sea invaded St. Clement's Road, Roseville Street and Green Street. Water also flowed down Plat Douet Road from Grande Charrière slip. Green Road and the Dicq were entirely under water, and the tide was across the inner road at First Tower. Much damage was done to gardens and walls around Le Bourg, while Green Island changed its shape slightly, the yellowish clay colouring the foaming sea in the vicinity as waves swept over the Island.

Elsewhere waves broke over the lantern of Corbière Lighthouse, and the sea flowed into St. Ouen's Pond. It was also across the road in the Gorey Pier area. Twenty-five yards of the Maison Victor Hotel wall at the Dicq were swept away, and many other walls were undermined when the sand level dropped six feet or more in places. Both the sea wall and road were gashed at Petit Port, Corbière, where monstrous waves were driven straight in by the gale. At the peak of the tide along the south coast, private steps were washed away, cars submerged and houses, shops and cellars flooded.

It is worth mentioning that during 1967 there were 22 tides with a higher predicted height — two of them being 40.1 feet. On 1 January, 1966 the datum was lowered by one foot, so the 38.7 tide of 2 November was equal to the old 37.7, and the 2.7 low water was equal to the old 1.7 prior to 1966. So there was nothing exceptional in the November tide as predicted. The cause was the cumulative effect of a long series of Atlantic depressions coinciding with a severe south-west gale, a fairly high spring tide and a very low barometer reading.

The sea breaking over the Esplanade wall, St. Helier. This scene no longer exists. It is now all reclaimed land.
(Photo Jersey Evening Post)

Granite stones from the Esplanade: flicked like breadcrumbs from the wall.
(Photo Jersey Evening Post)

At high water the wind was S.W. force 8, 42 miles per hour and the barometer 28.76 inches. At 9 a.m. the wind was W.S.W. force 8-9, the barometer was 29.0 inches and nearly one inch of rain had fallen in the previous 24 hours. The air temperature was 50°F and the sea water temperature 56°F. The whole of the Channel was a fury due to the gale and the long 'fetch' of the Atlantic rollers. The Portland Bill weather report for 6 a.m. was: wind west, 45 miles per hour, showers, barometer 975 millibars (28.8 inches). The centre of the depression was then over south Wales.

Although the strength of the wind, the height of the barometer and the predicted height of the tide were all outside record-breaking readings, the actual tide turned out to be one of the highest of the century. It is difficult to imagine what would have happened if a storm such as that experienced three years earlier had coincided with a 40 foot tide.

On Friday, 9 October, 1964, the sun rose through lowering clouds on a scene of complete stillness. The wind was calm, force 0, the sea was glassy calm and the smoke from the gasworks rose vertically into the sky over St. Helier. But a quick-moving and very intense depression came in from the west Channel and passed just north of Alderney. The wind increased through the Beaufort Scale to Force 12 in the early afternoon, when the tide was low. The highest gust, 108 miles per hour, was a record for the British Isles in October. Enormous damage was done across the Island. Many trees were uprooted, glasshouses smashed and buildings damaged.

At 3 p.m. the barometer was 28.59 inches, the lowest recorded at Maison St. Louis Observatory since 4 December, 1896 when it dropped to 28.36 inches. At the height of the storm, when the sea was a smother of foam and one-third of the water had been blown out of Havre des Pas bathing pool, the yacht *Mariecelia* en route from St. Malo to Jersey, capsized. The engines kept going and the yacht grounded near the Dog's

Nest off St. Helier Harbour. All perished save one girl, Miss Alison Mitchell, aged 20. Although no human being could have expected to survive for more than five minutes in such a sea, Miss Mitchell, in fact, drifted for the rest of the day and the whole of the night, finally dragging herself ashore at Petit Port, Egypt, on the north coast of the Island the following morning, and struggling up the path to Mr. W. A. de la Mare's Lower Egypt Farm. "I kept apologising to God for being a naughty girl," she said in hospital. Her survival was surely an epic of the sea without parallel in the history of the Channel Islands.

The sea comes up Gloucester Street, St. Helier. It can never happen again because there is no sea the other side of the wall. Gloucester Street is a fair way inland because of land reclamation. An underpass is now where the sea was for centuries. (Photo Jersey Evening Post)

LEVEL OF THE SEA

THERE IS MUCH TALK today of global warming and, in consequence, a rise in the level of the sea. Talks were given in the Island a few years ago suggesting a rise of three metres in the next fifty years. That would be the end of much of the parish of St. Helier and the parish of St. Clement to start with, but such talk is nonsense. The idea is to blame our manner of life with motor cars and gases in refrigerators, thus causing holes in the atmosphere. But such things as global warming and Ice Ages took place when people were living in mud huts with their families, and were confined to hunting.

The truth is that global warming has not started this century. The mean average world temperature is one degree higher than in 1900. That could be caused by heating in towns and cities. The level of the sea here has not changed for far more than a thousand years. This can be confirmed by the fact that there were rings in the walls of St. Helier Parish Church for fishermen to moor their boats. The church was built by the seashore where Helier was slain by pirates in 553 AD. Stand in Mulcaster Street by the church on a high spring tide, and the water in the harbour will be seen to be level with the church-yard.

Dr. John Renouf in his publication, *The First Farmers in the Channel Islands*, suggests that the sea level has not changed since 2,000-3,000 BC. He takes us back more than 10,000 years when the Ice Age was at its height. Then we were joined to Britain and France, and the River Seine flowed through the Hurd Deep off Alderney (where the yacht *Westward* belonging to T. B. Davis was sunk at his death) and the River Thames was part of the River Rhine.

After that, the sea level rose. Guernsey became an Island around 7,000 - 8,000 BC and Jersey around 4,000 - 5,000 BC. About 5,000 BC the high water spring tide was where our present low water spring tide is. That means that their low water spring tide was 80 feet lower than our high water spring tide is today. Much of the land between our high and low water was good for agriculture as were the lowlands in the Minquiers/Chausey area, but people preferred hunting and fishing, shellfish being particularly popular.

A mixed coniferous, mostly oak, forest covered a large area, and its remains can be seen on the rare occasions that the sand uncovers it south from l'Etacq at about high water neap tides. La Saline is the nearest slip. Dr. Renouf says that the beds are also exposed well down the beach between the Milano Bars and El Tico. They date from between 2,000 - 2,600 B.C. and are seen about once in fifteen years when the wind is right to remove the sand which preserves them.

The mild period which followed the Ice Age was checked about 1330 AD by the Little Ice Age. This generated violent storms in north-west Europe, and the archives of the Diocese of Coutances refer to widespread destruction of land around Le Moitiers d'Allonne just north of Carteret. It is also recorded that there was the overwhelming of land around Le Hocq and at the northern end of St. Ouen's Bay. This may have destroyed Le Manoir de la Brecquette at l'Etacq.

Dr. Renouf estimates the population of Jersey between 4,800 BC to 2,800 BC to have reached 2,000, while N.V.L. Rybot estimated a medieval population (13th - 14th centuries) of about 12,000.

The amount of water and water vapour in the world is constant. It is the ice in the world that varies, and that is why the sea level moves up and down. The melting of ice on land increases the level, while the Ice Ages see the level drop by

800 feet when we were joined to England and France. Millions of years ago there was no ice at the Poles, and therefore the percentage of water to earth was much greater.

In the Middle Ages there was both a warm period (when the Vikings came) and a Little Ice Age culminating about the 17th century, but the present trend is for ice to retreat. The Tree Line in Spitzbergen, north of Norway, is higher up the mountains, and glaciers such as the Fox in New Zealand and glaciers in the Rockies, are retreating. But these things can go into reverse. The cold of January 1994 in the United States was a record, while we had a mild winter. Americans were going in for another Ice Age, while we were muttering about global warming. It depends where you live. These things have all happened before, and there is no evidence of a serious change in world climate.

Nature has a self-correcting mechanism. If the sun is too powerful and causes skin cancer, a violent volcanic explosion will cause material to be flung many miles into the atmosphere and come between the sun and the earth, thus reducing the intensity of the sun, and lowering the temperature. Often notable sunrises and sunsets are observed.

The island of Krakatoa, near Java, was blown up by a volcano on 10 August, 1883. The explosion was heard 2,000 miles away in Australia, and was the loudest sound in history. An enormous tidal wave was caused. The lava and dust was blown twenty miles into the atmosphere, and the moon appeared blue for three years. Hence the expression, 'once in a blue moon.' We should look to natural phenomena, and such things as variation in the sun's output, for changes in climate rather than our manner of life.

We tend to take a grave view of drought, floods and extremes of cold and heat, and ponder on the imagined changes in climate. Elsewhere we have noted that if we take Jersey's rainfall in blocks of ten years, we have not had less than an average of 30 inches in any ten years. That is not far from the overall average of 33 inches.

With regard to temperature in the British Isles, the mean average has increased by one degree Farenheit since the turn of the century. So global warming has not started and the climate has not changed. But the extremes are thrilling, and give us something to write about. There is nothing to fear.

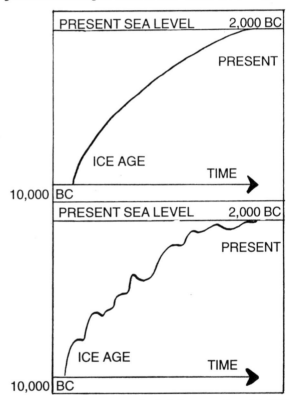

When the Ice Age was at its height more than 10,000 years ago, Jersey was part of France and England. The sea level then rose and Jersey became an island about 4,500 years ago. The sea level did not rise at a uniform rate as is suggested by the curve at the top. The lower chart shows an irregular rise until 2,000 BC. Since then there has been very little change.

THE GREAT STORM OF 1703

THE STORM OF 7-8 DECEMBER 1703 (new style calendar) was the worst in Britain since meteorological records began. The damage caused is almost beyond belief, and nothing like it has been caused since. It was said to be the remains of a West Indian hurricane. That is possible, although few are as late as December.

In an official report by Cambridge University Press it quotes Short as saying, 'England lost more ships than ever were lost in any encounter with the enemy.' Other reports specified that a fleet of 160-200 ships of the English Navy, with their victuallers and supply ships 'sheltering in the Downes' off Deal on the Kent coast, were scattered by the storm, and one third of all the seamen in the navy were lost on the night of 7-8 December — 10,000 men in all. Thirteen navy ships from Portsmouth were scattered and destroyed. Of the crowded and flooded Thames, Defoe wrote, 'it was a strange sight to see all the ships in the river blown away .... No anchors or landfast, no cables or moorings would hold them, the chains which lay across the river for the mooring of ships all gave way.'

Among the casualties was Henry Winstanley, the architect of the indestructable Eddystone Lighthouse. He went out with a team of men the night before in order to carry out repairs. The light shone as usual on that night but the lighthouse was later blown to pieces and destroyed, and only the Eddystone Rocks remained.

At the same time 'a tin ship' from Land's End with one man and two boys on board, was blown out to sea. They travelled under bare poles for 150 miles, and landed between two rocks on the Isle of Wight. It was calculated that the average speed between midnight and 8 a.m. was between 18 and 19 knots. A miraculous survival.

The storm caused a tidal wave to run up the River Severn, bringing the water eight feet higher than ever recorded before and flooding the country for miles around. A flooded warehouse in Bristol caused £150,000 of damage. More than 800 houses were reduced to rubble, and damaged thousands more. Windmills were destroyed by the hundred, and thousands of chimneys came down. Hundreds of thousands of trees were uprooted. A cow was blown into the top of a tree, and birds were knocked out of the air and hurled against buildings.

At least a hundred churches were damaged and three cathedrals. The demand for tiles was so great that the price went up from 21 shillings per thousand to £6 per thousand. But this was only for Britain. It also hit France and Sweden. Defoe says, 'The Baltic Sea — Finland, Muscovy and part of Tartary — until "at last it must lose itself in the vast Northern Ocean where Man never came and Ship never sailed".'

A series of depressions had moved from west to east for some time, and there was a jet stream at 60°-65° North. The main depression deepened to 950 millibars over the Midlands, and no observer had seen the glass so low. It was 965 millibars in London. The wind started in the south, veered to south-west and then north-west behind the cold front, and finally north. In Sweden the wind was east, and later west.

When the depression had gone through, the barometer rose rapidly, and reached 1031 millibars in Paris. The greatest damage, and the most severe winds occurred on the rising barometer. It did the same in Jersey when the trees came down in 1987. Also on 29 January, 1953, a depression near Iceland came down the North Sea and caused a tidal surge which flooded Holland and Canvey Island and was the cause of the Thames Barrage being built. A vast amount of damage would be caused if the Thames overflowed because certain areas are below river level, and there is a risk that London is sinking. But that great northerly storm and tidal surge was caused by a ridge of high pressure moving in behind the depression. The depression itself was not fatal, but the ridge following was.

There were many whirlwinds and tornadoes in Britain, France and Holland, as well as thunderstorms. In the Netherlands, Utrecht Cathedral was severely damaged and partly blown down. Many houses and churches and mills were badly damaged in Jutland which was particularly hard hit, and so were the Danish islands of Fyn and Sjaelland. Many ships ran aground on Jutland, and most houses were damaged or destroyed. In north Germany the biggest churches in Wismar, Rostock and Stralsund had their spires blown down.

The wind gusting to 108 miles per hour on 9 October, 1964 in Jersey did relatively little damage, so the average wind of 150 miles per hour on 8-9 December, 1703, seems reasonable, with gusts much higher. That is far above Force 12 on the Beaufort scale.

Jersey was in the thick of things, but because it was before newspapers came out, there is no written record of what happened here. It has come down by word of mouth that cows were blown into the air, and that is certainly possible as a cow was blown into the uttermost branches of a tree in Kent. There were almost certainly abnormal tides, and extensive damage to trees, birds, animals and buildings. Ships must have been sunk.

The nation accepted the cause to be the fierce anger of God through their manifold sins and wickedness. A service of repentance was held in December, 1704, and each year after there was a service and a distinguished preacher. The service was advertised as usual in December, 1822. It seems that the Lord accepted their true repentance extending over 119 years, because no storm like it has occurred since.

The same line of thought was taken in Jersey. Thirty years after the storm the steeple of St. John's church was struck by lightning and partially destroyed. It occurred on Sunday, 16 December, 1733, just before Matins. It gave the Rector a ready-made sermon. "Now do you see what the Lord thinks of you"? he raged.

La Société Jersiaise has no record of the storm recorded at the time, but a report of storm damage was made after a gale in 1787. The translation is as follows:

It would be necessary to possess a superhuman philosophy to conceive of the astonishing revolutions that the face of the globe has undergone from the beginning of time to the present; I do not mean political revolutions; it is of the natural that I would speak.

This little land that we inhabit affords us curious proofs enough. The tree trunks and roots that were uncovered during the winter of 1994/95 by the roughness of the sea in St. Ouen's Bay, are still visible and provide us with a subject of contemplation in very remote times. Thousands of trees are to be seen lying one by another in this bay, from Corbière to the two sandbanks some miles from high water. From these ancient remains it cannot be doubted that all this ground, as well as that above, called Les Mielles, was formerly rich grassland and dense forests, which were submerged by some extraordinary occurrence. Among these trees are to be seen some very large ones, and we are assured that after some storms, depending on the wind, they stand out so far above the sand that it is very difficult for carts to pass. It may be that the bays of St. Helier, St. Clement and Grouville, which are very extensive, have suffered the same fate, and that the sea, which is not rough in those places, does not reveal to us anything similar; for it is to be noted that only rarely, and after great winds, are those in St. Ouen's Bay rendered visible.

Dr. John Renouf comments that the only area that needs

updating is the age of the buried forest. We now know that this was Neolithic, dating significantly to 2,000 BC, the time we know from other evidence elsewhere in the world that the sea level plateaued off at more or less its present height. However, what we cannot ascertain from study of the physical evidence — as opposed to archival — is when the Neolithic forest was overrun by the sea. Of its nature such events are inclined to be destructive whether they occur by sudden violent storm from time to time — over decades, centuries, millenia perhaps — or by one triggering a sudden rise of tens of centi-metres in sea level. It is this uncertainty that makes the inter-pretation of what has happened around our coasts — and there are submerged forests in most of our bays and evidence of former land extent on places such as Icho Tower (Rybot 1928) — so difficult.

They may have been walls observed below the level of sand and even of soil on the low land between Les Lavers and L'Etacq, but this does not date the walls. The article makes a sound case, and I know this to be so from other evidence, that sand cover dates from a number of periods. I would not be at all surprised that the bulk of the Blanches Banques above the Neolithic horizon dates from as late as the 18th century. However, as another observer has pointed out, there is no evidence of good land having existed on Les Quennevais at any historical time past, and this would suggest that sand had covered this area sufficiently in prehistoric and/or early histori-cal times for it all to have been poor sandy soil. This was then overlain by an overwhelming event blowing the main sand of the Blanches Banques as late as the 18th century. The fact that fossil dunes are frozen in place and retain their original form and shape on the lower reaches of the Banques might be taken to indicate that the event is comparatively recent.

And to return to what is possibly a crucial interpretation — the date for significant loss of land — reported so clearly by Poingdestre in the late 17th century — at both St. Ouen and elsewhere in the Island, he dates this to the mid-14th century. This matches what we know about the rapid deterioration of climate in north-west Europe that began in the early decades of the 13th century from a wide swathe of sources.

At the end of the day, I subscribe to the views that there were significant encroachments of the sea over good and fertile land in the area south-west from l'Etacq in the 14th century continuing to a lesser extent right down to the height of the Little Ice Age in the 17th century. A major storm in 1703 would, to my way of thinking but without investigating the evidence, be a one-off event and unimportant in terms of the encroachments of the Middle Ages. But there well may have been a period of sand blowing in the 18th century on a large scale forming the important dunes.

COASTAL EROSION

ONE OF THE PROBLEMS about living in an island as opposed to a land mass is coastal erosion. Great storms which occur from time to time do enormous damage, and the cost of repairing walls is huge. There is talk of £40 million being needed over the next few years. This makes the £20 million needed to upgrade the Airport a triviality.

The trouble is that many walls are vertical – such as the walls at Greve d'Azette and at Gorey. This means that the wall takes the full force of water. The German wall at St. Ouen's, built of reinforced concrete and made to resist tanks and gun fire, has actually been bent in one place by the sea.

However, many walls are sloping, and that is far the best although it does not stop a drop in sand level. When that happens a vertical concrete wall is built to shore up the wall. The violence of the waves hitting it can shake houses. They should in future be sloping. Note that every bay (except Plémont and Beauport) has a sea wall. In the old days the sea found its level among the sand and bracken.

Very serious alarm is being caused by the disappearing sand. The level of sand along the promenade behind the Royal Jersey Golf Club was such that one could jump off the wall onto the sand. It has dropped by 13 feet since the war. There are several concrete walls propping it up at one point. The trouble is that a neap tide reaches the wall. A tide of 38 feet used to reach the top of the sand. Now one of 25 feet touches the wall which has to withstand water 15 feet deep with a tide of 40 feet which will occur in 1996. So the more the sand level drops, the greater the speed of undermining and erosion. A place called Sands in St. Ouen's Bay also has the sea reaching the wall on a neap tide.

We did not hear much about erosion before the war, but once the Germans started moving millions of tons of sand off Grouville and elsewhere for their fortifications, the trouble started. When we contemplate the vast numbers of concrete towers and walls around the Island, and then think of the amount of sand from off our coast in them, we can hardly wonder at the changes in our beaches. Add to that, the reclamation schemes at St. Helier Harbour and Havre des Pas when more sand came from St. Ouen's and Grouville bays, the true cost of these schemes is almost doubled by the amount of damage they cause.

It is said that even the building of a groyne causes changes in beaches, sometimes for several miles, although not every change is for the worse. However, in the case of Jersey, the beaches are our most precious possession and far too many have been ruined.

It has not been realised in high places how great our tides are because they are part of life. Any fortification or building which diverts the currents is bound to have a dramatic effect. I take the view that the root trouble was caused by the Germans and not by the States, because their movement of sand was so great that they had to build a railway from Gorey to Sorel and St. Ouen to transport it.

This is not the time to grizzle about what has happened but rather to find a way of putting things right. We might remember that Bournemouth spent £1 million on taking sand from Sandbanks, Poole, to raise the level of their wonderful beach by the promenade. Visitors are the key to their economic survival, and they did not hesitate. Nor should we, both for our visitors and residents.

A very precious part of the beach is the soft, white, dry sand at the top by the wall. This is because people like sun

Every bay in Jersey (except Plémont and Beauport) has a sea wall today. This is Green Island slip before the large sloping wall was built. The seaweed line marking high water is among the grasses by the boat. Today it is a car park, and there is Green Island Restaurant. Note that all the children and grown-ups are wearing hats.

bathing on it. The last thing we want are stones such as replaced the sand from the Dicq to the lighthouse in the winter of 1994-5. The white sand is, of course, covered by a spring tide.

This sand is often blown by gales off the beach on to the road and into houses. It causes very great changes in sand levels – in fact, wind as much as tide causes changes in sand levels. We must not always blame reclamation schemes. A violent gale has taken six feet of sand off Greve de Lecq in one tide, but it returns. There is a balance which is constant unless there is a major change caused by building breakwaters and that sort of thing.

Probably the building of sea walls is our basic error. Like King Canute, we are trying to stop the sea exercising its right to be up to Wharf Street and almost up to St.Ouen's Pond. We have taken on a mighty power. As it is, buildings worth hundreds of millions of pounds are where the sea, fish and seaweed lived and operated for thousand of years, and have now been replaced by hotels, car parks, bus stations, roads, shops and the electricity power station. We have reclaimed land from the sea on a big scale, and therefore part of our Island is artificial. We have to pay the penalty.

EARTHQUAKES IN THE CHANNEL ISLANDS

Earthquakes or earth tremors have been recorded in Jersey on the following dates and scale of intensity:

Date	Scale	Date	Scale
24 Oct 842	8	14 Mar 1880	
2 Nov 1091	8	26 Aug 1884	4
1 Jan 1161		7 Jun 1886	3.5
29 Mar 1750	7	20 Apr 1887	5
14 Aug 1761		30 May 1889	7
15 Apr 1773	7	8 July 1889	
16 Apr 1773		21 Apr 1901	
23 Apr 1773		2 Feb 1904	4
27 Sep 1791		8 Jan 1914	4
25 Jan 1799	8	10 Aug 1923	4
23 Sep 1804		1 Feb 1925	6
29 Jul 1832	6	30 Jul 1926	8
10 Mar 1843		17 Feb 1927	7
22 Dec 1843	6	21 Aug 1927	3
1 Apr 1853	7	19 Nov 1927	
4 Apr 1868	8	23 Dec 1928	5
3 Jan 1872		11 Nov 1930	
23 Aug 1872		16 Nov 1930	
21 Aug 1877		12 Apr 1933	
27 Jan 1878	7	30 Apr 1990	3.5
11 Mar 1880			

In the scale for Jersey, Scale 8 means that chimneys are thrown down and there are cracks in the walls of houses. But Scale 8 on the Richter Scale of today means a major severe earthquake killing many thousands of people.

1. Recorded only by instruments.
2. Felt only by a few persons lying down and sensitive to weak tremors.
3. Felt by ordinary persons at rest; not strong enough to disturb loose objects.
4. Windows, doors, fire-irons etc. made to rattle.
5. The observer's seat perceptibly raised or moved.
6. Chandeliers, pictures etc. made to swing.
7. Ornaments, vases etc. overthrown.
8. Chimneys thrown down and cracks in the walls of some, but not many houses, in one place.
9. Chimneys thrown down and cracks made in the walls of about one-half the houses in one place.

THE JERSEY EARTHQUAKE OF 30 JULY, 1926

According to the late Dr. G. H. Plymen the earthquake of 30 July, 1926, at 2.20 p.m. B.S.T., was of the order of Scale 8. There were three others of that order, 1091, 1799 and 1868, so we must reasonably assume that it was as bad as any in the past. As there is no record of anyone being killed, or house destroyed, at any time, we can say that the Island is not in a dangerous earthquake zone. Small tidal waves are sometimes observed, caused by under-water tremors.

There is no need for our buildings to be of the strength of those in San Francisco or Japan, but the building trade might well assume that we could get an earthquake twice as severe as that of 30 July, 1926, and build accordingly, while reservoirs here are probably built to endure an earthquake, three or four times as severe. As it is, there are seismographs at Val de la Mare and Queen's Valley reservoirs, and other places, and they are monitored daily. Each day there are some slight

The top of the steeple of St. Columbia's Presbyterian church, Midvale Road, displaced by an earthquake in 1926. The steeple was removed a few years ago as it was regarded as being unsafe, probably because it was weakened by the earthquake. Grouville church steeple was also damaged.

movements, but they do not qualify as earth tremors. Somewhere in the world there are movements, and they are picked up here, but not felt.

The shock on 30 July, 1926, was felt near Coutances on the Normandy coast, Guernsey and Sark. Dr. Plymen adds 'unfortunately, in the absence of instruments, and of experienced observers, as well as an absence of evidence from the sea, it is unlikely that accurate estimates can be made.' It is believed that the epi-centre was near the Ecrehous. Père Rey had not set up his seismograph then.

Experiences of observers are as follows:

1. Mr. C. Maxwell Hibbert. Servant-staff in the kitchen of Victoria Club felt swaying motion. Rumbling noise like that of a heavy lorry close by.
2. Mr. R. Bisson, Burrard Street. Noise like an explosion of thousands of tons of earth falling. House trembled seeming to sink slightly downwards. Man thrown two feet. Zig-zag crack in wall on west side.
3. Mr. E. Morris, then staying at St. Cyr Hotel. While resting on a bed, felt it shake violently for two seconds. Shock as if hotel were charged by heavy lorry. The whole building swayed and observer expected it to collapse.
4. Dental Surgeon, St. Mark's Road, obliged by vibration to cease work. Attributed noise to gas explosion. Noise from south-west.
5. Lady thrown off bicycle while cycling past St. Mark's church, St. Mark's Road.
6. Steeple of Presbyterian Church, Midvale Road, shifted, as regards two upper sections, to north-east.
7. Man in field, Mont-au-Prêtre, saw tomato canes swayed by the shock.
8. Workmen at Elizabeth Castle stated that the sound

came from the south-west.

9.   Mr. A. K. Faed, Longueville. Sound like passing of heavy lorry sensation of an east-and-west movement lasting ten seconds.
10. Mr. Mourant, Maison de Haut, Longueville, St. Saviour. Sound like distant guns. House shook for ten seconds. Seemed to show a north-and-south movement.
11. Steeple of Grouville church shifted, in topmost section, to north-east.
12. Commander McEwen, St. Ouen's Bay. Sound like heavy lorry on the road, or like passage of an underground train. Shock lasted two or three seconds.

The earthquake at Kobe, Japan, in 1994 killed 5,000 people and was 6.8 on the Richter Scale, but the one in 1923 in Tokyo was Scale 8 and killed 200,000 people. There was also a major earthquake in Quetta, India, now Pakistan, on 1 September, 1929.

It is impossible to visit Portugal without hearing the Lisbon earthquake of 1755 mentioned by guides. Much of the city was destroyed, and waves 60 feet high drowned hundreds of people. Inland waters like Loch Lomond was disturbed, the surface of which rose and fell almost a yard every ten minutes for an hour and a half. An earthquake at Agidir, West Africa, sent a tidal wave right across the Atlantic Ocean. One in Chile caused giant waves to carry warships two miles inland.

So, once again, Jersey is exceedingly fortunate to be spared earthquakes and tidal waves. We are spared worry and anxiety, but millions of people live on a bomb.

Statistically, the Island is due for a sharp earth tremor.

'LE CANON DES ILES'

EVERY GENERATION of Jerseymen for hundreds of years has occasionally heard a low rumbling sound from France rather like gunfire, blasting or an earthquake. Nobody has ever solved it.

The sound is most common in summer when the barometer is high and there is a light north-east wind. In these days of noise pollution by aircraft and cars, it is difficult to detect, but there are still people who hear it, so it continues as always.

The general tendency is to link it with the sea, but it has nothing to do with the tidal condition at a specific time. If that was so, the problem would have been solved immediately. Blasting, gunfire and earthquakes can easily be checked. No volcanic action has been revealed.

The first written evidence was by the Norman diarist Sire de Gouberville on 2 July, 1652, but it was probably heard but not recorded for several centuries before that. It is heard in France just as frequently, and speculation as to what it is often occurs in French newspapers and magazines.

Yachts in the vicinity of Les Ecréhous have reported down the years. It would help if yachtsmen noted it in the log because they are the most likely to hear it in calm weather when there is no noise pollution.

Le Canon des Iles is part of our heritage. Something causes it. In these days of computers, recording apparatus and seismographs we should be capable of solving something which has defeated our forefathers.

WHAT THE BIBLE SAYS

ONE OF THE VERY INTERESTING THINGS about the Creation is that at the beginning there was not such a thing as rain. In the first book of the Bible, Genesis, chapter 2 verses 4,5,6 and 7 it says,

'These are the generations of the heavens and of the earth when they were created, in the day that the Lord God made the earth and the heavens, and every plant of the field before it was in the earth, and every herb of the field before it grew; for the Lord had not caused it to rain upon the earth, and there was not a man to till the ground. But there went up a mist from the earth, and watered the whole face of the ground.

And the Lord God formed man of the dust of the ground, and breathed into his nostrils the breath of life; and man became a living soul.'

So there was not such a thing as a rainbow.

After God destroyed mankind by flood — Noah's Flood — he regretted it and made a promise: "While the earth remaineth, seedtime and harvest, and cold and heat, and summer and winter, and day and night shall not cease" (Genesis chapter 8 verse 22). That is the first promise ever made by God and it is known as the First Covenant. To prove it and to remind us, he put a rainbow in the sky. So we have rain.

The next thing to consider is Joseph's dream. After Benjamin, he was the youngest of the twelve sons of Jacob who was renamed Israel.

He dreamed that there would be seven years of plenty and seven years of famine in the days of Pharaoh. They came to pass. Dreams are a form of communication. So days of plenty and great droughts happened from early days, and continue to the present. We should not think that the climate is changing when long periods of a certain type persists.

There are stories of drought and floods in the days of Elijah, and a lack of water with Moses in the wilderness when he struck the rock. Sudden storms in the Sea of Galilee still occur today.

The word 'water' occurs in the Bible an enormous number of times, and there is much talk of wells to water the sheep, of rivers and streams, and of the river of Eden to water the Garden of Eden. The simple fact is that without water everything dies. It is one of the four vital elements — earth, air, water and fire.

We often find that Easter is cold. Turning to the Bible, St. John chapter 18 verse 18, we note that at the trial of Jesus before Pilate, there was a fire. Peter denied that he knew Jesus. 'And the servants and officers stood there, who had made a fire of coals; for it was cold: and they warmed themselves: and Peter stood with them, and warmed himself'.

Easter is the first Sunday after the full moon; next after 21 March, the fourteenth night of the moon.

Jesus, the Light of the World, was crucified at the vernal — spring — equinox when the sun is vertical to the equator, and the whole earth has an equal amount of light and darkness. There was a star at his birth and a full moon at his death. This enabled there to be an eclipse of the sun which can occur only with a full moon: 'And there was darkness over the whole land'. Forces and powers outside the earth prevailed.

In 1996 Easter Day is 7 April; 1997: 30 March; 1998: 12 April; 1999: 4 April and 2000: 23 April.

WEATHER LORE

The oldest saying is:

Red sky at night, shepherds' delight
Red sky in the morning, shepherd's warning.

The words were quoted in effect by Jesus Christ in St. Matthew chapter 16 verse 2. He said, "When it is evening, ye say, 'it will be fair weather for the sky is red." And in the morning, "it will be foul weather today for the sky is red and lowering."
It could be that it was said in the time of Jacob, or Israel, 4,000 years ago, because shepherds were out 'keeping watch over their flock by night' as well as the day. Shepherds and sailors have unrivalled knowledge of the weather.

An English summer — two hot days and a thunderstorm.

Three days of ground frost, then it will rain.

In summer a fog from the south, warm weather; from the north, rain.

Summer comes with a bound; winter comes yawning.(Finland)

As the days begin to shorten,The heat begins to scorch them.

Winter never died in the ditch.

A green winter makes a fat churchyard.

When there is a spring in the winter, or a winter in the spring, the year is never good.

Too fine a winter will swamp the summer.

If the ice will bear a goose before Christmas, it will not bear a duck after.

The blackest month in all the year is January.

January warm — the Lord have mercy!
(Because a premature growth of vegetation is liable to suffer severe damage from spring frosts).

An English winter ends in July, to begin again in August.

As the day lengthens, So the cold strengthens.

When oak trees bend with snow in January, good crops may be expected.

January, freeze the pot by the fire,

February fill dyke.

A warm January, a cold May.

Fair on St. Paul's Conversion Day, 25 January, is favourable to all fruit.

February, shortest and worst of all months. (France)

All the months of the year curse a fair February.

The Welshman would rather see his dam on the bier
Than see a fair February.

One would rather see a wolf in February than a peasant
in his shirt sleeves. (Germany)

2 February: The shepherds would rather see the wolf
enter his fold on Candlemas Day than the sun. (Germany)

If Candlemas Day be fair and bright
Winter will have another flight.
But if Candlemas Day bring clouds and rain
Winter is gone and won't come again.

14 February: To St. Valentine the spring is a neighbour.
(France)

Better to be bitten by a snake
Than to feel the sun in March. (Wiltshire)

March comes in like a lion and goes out like a lamb.

March is traditionally a boisterous month throughout the temperate zones of the northern hemisphere. The reason is that the polar regions are then about at their coldest after nearly six months of night while the equatorial regions are at their hottest because the sun is overhead. The strength of the atmospheric circulation depends primarily on the difference of temperature between the equator and the poles; hence it is most vigorous when the contrast of heat and cold are greatest – in March.

When March has April weather, April will have March
weather. (France)

March winds and April showers bring forth May flowers.

1 April: If it thunders on All Fool's Day
It brings good crops of corn and hay.

For a warm May the parsons pray;
A hot May makes a fat churchyard. (Chaucer)

Cast not a clout till May be out.

A wet May will fill a barn full of hay;
A cold May gives full barns and empty churchyards.

17 to 19 May, St.Dunstan: St. Dunstan is alleged to have set up business as a brewer, and to have bartered his soul to the devil in return for an annual spring frost severe enough to blast the apple crop and so put a stop to the production of cider – the rival drink to beer.

12 to 15 July: Buchan's first warm period.

15 July, St. Swithin: If it rains on St. Swithin's Day it will rain
for 40 days. The weather will be foul for 40 days.

12 to 15 August: Buchan's second warm period.

15 August, Assumption: On St. Mary's Day sunshine
Brings much and good wine.

14 September, Holyrood:
The passion flower blossoms about this time.
(The flower is said to present a resemblance to the cross or rood; the nails, the crown of thorns used at the Crucifixion).

Full moon in October without a frost, no frost till full moon in November.

18 October, St. Luke: *St. Luke's little summer.*
(By official averages October's last week is the wettest of the year in Southern England. The chances of a completely dry day about 28 October are at a minimum).

November: *If ice in November will bear a duck*
Then the rest of the winter will be rain and muck.

Halloween: *If ducks do slide at Hallotide*
At Christmas they will swim;
If ducks do swim at Hallotide
At Christmas they will slide.

11 November, St. Martin:

If All Saint's Day will bring out the winter,
St. Martin's Day will bring out Indian summer
If the geese on Martin's Day stand on ice,
They will walk in mud at Christmas. (France)

One bleak morning in early November (so the legend runs) St. Martin, Bishop of Tours, gave half his cloak to a poor man shivering from cold. Seeing this, the Good Lord who sees all good things, set the sun shine warmly until the saint could get another garment. It was ordained that in commemoration of Martin's kind deed a spell of fair and mild weather should evermore occur during the early part of November.

21 December, Winter solstice
Frost on the shortest day is said to indicate a severe winter.

A green Christmas makes a fat churchyard.

At Christmas meadows green, at Easter covered with frost.

The shepherd would rather see his wife enter the Stable than sun.

25 December, Christmas Day:
Christmas wet, empty granary and barrel.

If it snows during Christmas night, the crops will do well.

If ice will bear a man before Christmas, it will not bear a mouse afterwards.

When the blackbird sings before Christmas, she will cry before Candlemas.

June – too soon;   July – stand by;
August – look out you must;   September – remember
October – all over
(Hurricanes in the West Indies quoted by Admiral Nares).

The sudden storm last three hours.

When the wind is in the east
'Tis neither fit for man nor beast;
When the wind is in the north
The ardent fisher goes not forth;
When the wind is in the south
It blows the bait into the fish's mouth;
When the wind is in the west
Then it's at its very best.

A dappled sky, like a painted woman, soon changes it face.
(France)

4,000 telephone lines, 20 poles and many electricity cables down. Ten inches of snow offically measured at the Airport, 28 February 1962.

Mackerel sky, mackerel sky,
Never long wet, never long dry
Mares' tails and mackerel sky,
Not long wet, not long dry.
(Berkshire)

It is better to dwell in the corner of the housetop, than with a brawling woman in a wide house on a very rainy day.

When clouds appear like rocks and towers
The Earth's refreshed by frequent showers.

A very clear sky without clouds is not to be trusted, unless the barometer is high.

The farther the sight, the nearer the rain.

When the Isle of Wight is clearly seen from Brighton or Worthing, expect rain soon.

A good hearing day is a sign of wet.

Sound travelling far and wide: A stormy day will betide.

Sounds are heard with unusual clearness before a storm; The railway whistle, for instance, seems remarkable shrill.

Waterspouts are not produced in cold weather.

Rain before seven; fine before eleven.

The morning sun never lasts the day.

Moonlit nights have the hardest frosts.

The moon and the weather may change together
But change of the moon does not change the weather.
If we'd no moon at all and that may seem strange
We still should have weather that's subject to change.

When rain comes before the wind
Halyards, sheets, and braces mind;
But when wind comes before the rain,
Soon you may make sail again. (Fitzroy)

A veering wind, fair weather; A backing wind, foul weather.

If the wind veers from north to north-east in winter, intense cold follows.

Rain long foretold, long last; Short notice, soon past.

After great droughts come great rains.

A white frost never stays more than three days.

Early frost are usually followed by a long and hard winter.

Snow cherisheth the ground and anything sowed in it.

An eight-day mantle of snow is like a mother to the earth, but if it lasts longer it is like a mother-in-law. (France)

Lightning brings heat.
(Lightning on its way through the air produces ammonia and nitrogen oxides. The ammonia dissolved in rain, becomes ammonium hydroxide — a plant food. The nitrogen oxide reacts with atmospheric moisture to form nitric and nitrous acids, which, as soluble nitrates, fertilise the soil. Hence a thundery summer tends to favour crops).

Rapid fall after high, sun at last and very dry;
First rise after low, foretells a stronger blow.

15 September is said to be fine six years out of seven. Support for this statement from modern statistical work showing that the odds against rain on this day between 7 a.m. and midnight in London are greater around mid-September than at any other period of the year.

28 October is the wettest. The chances of a completely dry day are at a minimum. By official averages October's last week is the wettest of the year.

Last night the sun went pale to bed
The moon in haloes hid her head.
T'will surely rain — I see with sorrow
Our jaunt must be put off tomorrow.

He who shears his sheep before St. Servatius's Day — 11 May — loves his wool more than his sheep. (Because it is still cold).

WEATHER AND THE CALENDAR

IN THE YEAR 46 BC, Julius Caesar decided that a year was 365¼ days, so he gave every fourth year an extra day, and called it Leap Year. But it was too much because the actual time for the earth's journey round the sun is 365 days, 5 hours, 48 minutes 46 seconds. Pope Gregory XIII found in 1582 that the spring (vernal) equinox was 11 March instead of 21 March, so he directed that the day after 4 October, 1582, should be 15 October. He also directed that three times in 400 years, the Leap Year arrangements should be omitted. This corrected an 11 minute 14-second discrepancy, or one day every 128 years.

So any year ending in two noughts would not be a Leap Year unless it could be divided by 400. Thus 1700, 1800 and 1900 were not Leap Years, but 2000 will be because we can divide it by 400.

The Protestant nations did not take to the Gregorian new-style calendar until 1752, when it was then necessary to leave out 11 days. Today it would mean 12 days, or nearly a fortnight. Russia did not adopt it until 1917. The October revolution actually took place on 7 November.

There were indignant meetings of people in 1752 when the day following 2 September was 14 September, and there were shouts of 'give us back our 11 days.' The effect was to bring Christmas forward, and everything else forward, by 11 days.

Up to 1752, New Year's Day was 25 March or Lady Day. The first AD calendar was said to begin with the conception of Christ, not the birth, on 25 March. It is known as the Supputation of our Lord. Although we sing of Christ coming down from heaven on Christmas Day, it is nonsense. He came down from heaven when the angel overshadowed the Virgin Mary on 25 March. From then on he was here on Earth in the womb. So the year started (AD) on 25 March until 1752 when it was moved to 1 January.

All this has caused an immense change in the timing of the weather. Although we sing on St. Stephen's Day 26 December 'all the snow lay round about, deep and crisp and even,' we know that it seldom happens. But if St. Stephen's Day was 7 January, as it used to be, then the risk of snow would be very real, and a white Christmas very much on the cards. As it is, the Eastern Orthodox Church celebrates Christmas on 6 January (Twelfth Night) to this day, and Russia did until 1917.

A lot of our weather lore is based on the pre-Julian calendar, and our instinctive expectation throughout the year is geared to this. It is part of 'the knowing' — the pre-birth knowledge which we bring into the world, and which goes back in time to the dim distance.

We can sit and think of the things which would happen if everything was eleven days later. For one thing, there would never be a March Easter — it would be in April or early May. The farmers would still catch it then because the weather is the same; it's the calendar that has changed.

What it boils down to is that the whole year has been shifted, as it were, to the right. The spring is colder than it should be and the autumn warmer. In simple language, when the temperature is 82°F (28°C) on 1 September we should remember that it should be 20 August; when Easter is bitterly cold on 25 March it should be 14 March. It is the basic cause of our muttering that the weather is not what it was in the old days.

TRAVEL BY SEA

Anyone in London wishing to visit Jersey two hundred years ago would take a horse and carriage to a south coast port — but more probably Southampton or Weymouth, stopping for refreshment at inns on the way — and find a sailing vessel leaving for the Island. The journey could take at least three days if the vessel became becalmed. The journey was hazardous as there was no radio, no radar, no lighthouses and hardly a port worthy of the name. On landing in Jersey at anything but high water, passengers were carried ashore on the backs of men. There was no dredging.

There was no mailboat in those days. Letters were handed to merchants or coffee house keepers and then to the captain of a ship who in turn handed them to the receiving agent. They went by mailcoach to various places and were charged by distance. The catch was that the recipient paid the postage.

The cost of a single-page letter to Scotland in 1815 was one shilling (5p) which was one tenth of a man's wages, so any Jersey family living in Scotland cringed when the postman was seen coming up the path. A two-page letter cost double.

In 1797 one Charles Le Geyt held the post of letters in his house, but he could not bear people banging at his door after 9 p.m. after opening at 8 a.m. So a woman named Mary Godfray tramped round St. Helier delivering letters for 6 shillings per week (30p). After 45 years she retired worn out in public service and asked for a pension. The request was refused. She was the first person to deliver letters in Jersey.

The General Post Office was located as follows:

1794-1827	Hue Street
1827-1842	Minden Place
1842-1843	The Old Parsonage now The Deanery
1843-1852	Bond Street
1852-1881	Queen Street
1881-1909	Halkett Place
1909-1971	Broad Street
1971-1996	Mont Millais
1996-	Rue des Près, St. Saviour

The coming of steam totally changed the form and speed of travel. The first steamer ever seen in Jersey and Guernsey was the paddle steamer *Medina*, 130 tons, hired by a Colonel Fitzgerald. Thousands flocked to see the monster belching smoke. The first railway reached Southampton in 1840 and brought the journey from London down to three hours. That finished the stage coach journeys. Southampton boomed while Weymouth suffered greatly during the seventeen years of wrangling before the railway arrived on 20 January, 1857. The line was broad gauge of 5 feet which meant changing trains at Bristol, but the standard gauge of 4 feet 8.5 inches was finally adopted some years later.

The first unofficial mailboat from Weymouth was the sailing ship *Royal Charlotte* which arrived on 18 February, 1794. She was a mere 67 tons compared with the *Caesarea* of 4,174 tons of the 1960's and 1970's. The *Royal Charlotte* took 16 hours in fine weather to cover the 85 miles from Weymouth.

It should be said from the beginning that the mail attracted thieves and robbers. Masters and crew often had cutlasses and swords to defend their ships. In 1793 war with France caused the Channel Islands to lose two thirds of their ships, and 900 passengers were taken prisoner. On 29 October, 1811, the *Chesterfield* was attached and captured by a Cherbourg privateer, the *L'Epruvier* mounting 14 guns with a crew of 50. The mails and dispatches were sunk prior to the boarding of the enemy.

An American privateer with 20 guns and 180 crew captured the *Brilliant*. A prize crew was put on board and she headed for France, but mistook Alderney harbour for the French port of La Hocque. She was promptly recaptured. And so we could go on.

The first official mailboat under steam was the *Watersprite* of 162 tons. She arrived on 7 July, 1827. Sir Colin Halkett, Lieutenant Governor of Jersey – hence Halkett Place – was very keen on the mail being brought by steam because of the speed. Incidently, there were no pillar boxes in the Island at that time, but the first arrived a few years later.

The steam mailboats operated from Weymouth thereafter. The cost of a single fare was:

	£	s.	d.	
Cabin passengers, each	1	1	0	(£1.05p)
Female servant, each		15	0	(75p)
Male servant, each		12	6	(62.5p)
Dogs		2	6	(12.5p)

The mailboats flew the Royal Mail flag which raised their status immediately because Her Majesty's mail had absolute priority over ships, stage coaches and trains. The night mail train from London to Glasgow, now discontinued, on which letters were sorted all night and mailbags picked up and put down en route at high speed, seldom faced a red light. Jersey people did not ask if the boat had arrived, but whether the mailboat had arrived. It carried the previous day's newspapers, essential cargo and passengers. The *Evening Post* always said,

'among the passengers travelling to Weymouth (or Southampton) this morning were ....' Anybody who was anybody got a mention.

The timing of the arrival and departure of the mailboats depended on the weather. In October, 1846, the paddle ship *Wonder* left Southampton at 7 p.m. in fair weather under Captain James Goodridge. A violent storm developed at 11 p.m. and when off the Casquets she was struck by a sea which carried away part of her bulwarks and did other damage. Many of the passengers were dashed from their berths to the floor of the cabin – and all were shut from the decks, as were the crew who were not on the bridge. By brilliant seamanship the Captain brought her to Guernsey where many Jersey passengers deemed it prudent to land. Captain Goodridge decided to proceed to Jersey where crowds gathered to cheer him. A public subscription was opened and he was presented with a silver trumpet and a piece of plate. There is an oil painting in the Museum depicting *Wonder* in this terrible storm.

This storm has been detailed at length because it occurred in October and was similar to that of 9 October, 1964, when the day started calm but hit the highest gust ever recorded in Britain in October i.e. 108 miles per hour at lunch time.

There were very many sinkings in those days, often because of fog. *HMS Cuckoo* was a fishing protection vessel at *Gorey* when the oyster trade was at its height and there were some violent scenes with the French (has anything changed?) She was on the mail run on 14 May, 1850, when she struck the Oyster Rock off Elizabeth Castle. She sank in the harbour entrance but was refloated.

On 17 March, 1870, the Normandy, 600 tons capable of 15.5 knots, was involved in a collision in fog with the 1,400 ton Baltic trader *SS Mary* with a cargo of Indian corn. She rose above the *Normandy* and fell across her decks. The *Normandy* sank in 20 minutes with the loss of Captain Harvey and 33 others. The mails were lost save one floating bag. The letters were dried out and delivered. A monument to this tragedy was erected in 1871 and is now to be seen between the Victoria Pier and Mount Bingham.

On 30 March, 1899, the *Stella* left Southampton for Guernsey at 4.10 p.m. with passengers coming home for Easter. Fog developed, patchy at first, and Captain Riggs reduced speed but resumed full speed later only to hit the Black Rock of the Casquets. The *Lynx* rescued 46 passengers and the *Vera* 64. Mrs. Mary Rogers, a stewardess, gave her lifebelt to a passenger and perished. There is a memorial window panel to her in Liverpool Cathedral. There is no doubt that the ship was racing the Weymouth boat although it was denied. It put an end to racing for all time. The *Stella* was a fine new modern ship when launched in 1890.

We now come to ships which live in the memory of some. The *Ibex*, built by Laird Brothers of Birkenhead for the Great Western Railway Company, could carry 600 passengers. She broke the speed record held by the *Lydia* and touched 20 knots. She was launched in 1891, and had two masts and two funnels. In 1897 she struck the Normontaise Rock off Jersey, and her passengers were landed at Portelet plus horses. She was towed to St. Aubin's Fort and St. Helier by the *Reindeer*. Captain Le Feuvre was suspended. In January, 1900, she struck a rock off Platte Fougère, Guernsey, and on 18 April, 1914, the *Ibex* collided with a disabled schooner off Portland. On 19 September, 1917, she collided with, and sank, the GWR cargo steamer *Aletta* twenty miles off Weymouth. The *Ibex* was replaced by the *St. Julien*.

The *Vera* was built for the London and South-Western Railway in 1998. During 1914-18 War she sank a German U-Boat by gunfire. She served on the Jersey - St. Malo run with the Southern Railway in 1932 when the railways became SR, GWR, LMS, LNER and Highlands.

The *Princess Ena* was built in 1908 for the Southampton - Channel Islands - St. Malo service. She struck the Paternosters in 1908 and the Minquiers in 1923. In 1935 she caught fire off Corbière and sank, the passengers being taken off by the *St. Julien*.

The first *Caesarea* was built by Cammel Laird in 1910. She could carry 980 passengers at 20.5 knots. She struck a rock off Noirmont in 1923, and then the Oyster Rock off Elizabeth Castle, sinking just outside the harbour mouth. The first *Sarnia* built in 1910 was torpedoed and sunk in 1918 by a German U-Boat.

The *Lorina* was built in 1918 and came to Jersey in 1920. She struck a rock in the small roads and was badly damaged in 1935. She was famous under Captain Light. The ship was sunk by German bombers at Dunkirk in 1940.

The *St. Helier* and *St. Julien* were GWR ships on the Weymouth run. They were built by John Brown of Clydebank who built the Cunard liner *Queen Mary*, 86,000 tons, known as the 534. They had two red funnels, later reduced to one. The *Isles of Jersey, Guernsey* and *Sark* had one yellow funnel and then two. The *St. Helier* brought out 10,200 troops and 1,500 refugees from Dunkirk in 1940 under Captain R. R. Pitman. He received the Distinguished Service Cross and was made M.B.E.

The *St. Julien* came to Jersey on 25 May, 1925, and was involved in the evacuation of troops from Dunkirk, Boulogne and Cherbourg. She was sent to the Mediterranean in 1943 and was at the Anzio landing in 1944. She struck a mine on D-Day plus one. Her final voyage to Jersey was on 27 September, 1960. Her commanders included Captains C. H. Langdon who died on board, J. Goodchild, L. T. Richardson (for 25 years) and R. R. Pitman D.S.C., M. B. E.

The *Isles of Jersey* and *Guernsey* built by the Denny Brothers in 1930 were of 2,143 tons and could carry 1,400 passengers at 19.5 knots. They also built the *Isle of Sark* in 1932. The *Isle of Jersey* came to Jersey on 13 March, 1931, under Captain Holt. Her last voyage was on 31 October, 1959. During the war she served as a naval hospital ship and made eleven crossings to the invasion beaches.

The *Isle of Guernsey* was involved at Dunkirk, bringing back 836 wounded men, and was the second vessel to enter Arromanches after D-Day. She made her last voyage from Southampton in May, 1961, when Southampton was closed to passenger traffic from the Channel Islands. Southampton was the most famous port for Jersey for two hundred years. Weymouth claimed to be the shortest sea crossing but Southampton claimed that the sea journey ended at the Needles! Southampton retains her historic link with the Channel Islands through Eastleigh Airport which has now been upgraded to become one of the most modern in Britain.

The *Brittany*, built by Denny Brothers of Dumbarton for the Southern Railway was of 1,522 tons and capable of carrying 850 passengers at 16 knots. She worked mainly on the St. Malo service and was known to bring in 850 Breton workers for the potato season. A popular ship, she was involved at Dunkirk in 1940 and saw service in West Africa, Seychelles, Panama and Bombay and was involved in the invasion of southern France. Among her commanders were Captains Withers, Trout, Campbell, Caws, Breuilly and Picot.

The difficulty of naming commanders is that it is never just one. For example, Captain Bernard Picot, still happily among us, commanded, at least for a time, the *Hilary, Ringwood, Haslemere, Hythe, Whitstable, Winchester, Noose, Elk, Maid of Kent, Normannia, Isle of Sark, Isle of Guernsey, Caesarea, Sarnia* and, for the longest, the *Brittany*.

It is sad that British Rail withdrew the *Brittany* from the French service just as people were finding the courage and the money to visit the Continent. Now there is a huge trade run by the French.

Finally, the *Caesarea* and the *Sarnia* came in 1960 and 1961 and were the last word in luxury and comfort. They could carry 1,400 passengers and offered double and single cabins and 44 sleeping berths. They cost £1,500,000 compared with nearly £20 million for the latest fast ships. British Rail gave up, and the car ferry took their place. The word 'mailboat' has gone.

Two hundred years ago less than one thousand people came to the Island. In 1993 a total of 1,353,000 people arrived by sea and air. Such a number would be impossible to handle without the Airport. The most humble apology is due to the airport for the lack of space given to it in this book. One can only say that aircraft no longer land on the beach and are not therefore subject to the tides! Nevertheless, aircraft are subject to weather of all kinds, and due honour must be given to the brilliance of captains and crew.

The Airport was built in 1937 and there have been only two major accidents. One was before the war when an aircraft took off into low cloud in warm sector conditions, and turned in cloud too quickly before there was enough speed. The aircraft slipped to the ground and all perished plus one man in a field.

The second aircraft also approached in fog in a warm sector one Holy Week. It came from Paris and the pilot was so accurate in his navigation that he struck one of the poles carrying a light on the approach to the runway. He struck it six feet from the top — the height of a man or woman. All died save one stewardess.

If we think of the hundreds of thousands of aircraft that have landed on the airfield, many before there were navigational aids, it is an astonishing record. We must also count the remarkably high standard of servicing, the quality of the aircraft, the care of those who check the fuel for quality several times a day, and the competence of control officers and meteorological staff.

The captain and crew of aircraft have to cope with fog, snow, ice accretion, gales, crosswind, thunderstorms and wet runways. There is also the hazard of sudden changes of wind direction, perhaps with the passage of a front as the aircraft is on its final approach. Braking is affected by water and ice. there is also the danger of overloading in very hot weather which means the air is lighter and cannot support the same weight as cold air. Putting an aircraft on the tarmac very early for morning take-off can mean dew forming and then freezing, affecting control surfaces.

There was a lighthouse at Les Quennevais in the early years to show where the airport was. Aircraft took off and landed on a green light from the control tower. Messages giving the weather and orders from the control tower were sent by Morse Code and received by the radio operator who passed them to the pilot. Radio telephone and navigational aids came slowly. One aid was 'coming in on a string.' The pilot picked up a signal which was a straight line to the airfield. If he drifted to the left he got dashes and if to the right he got dots. As was said elsewhere, when the pilot of the newspaper aircraft landed with a thud in thick fog, the pilot was asked how he did it. "Oh, no trouble," he replied dangling a cigarette, "I let down over St. Aubin's Bay, flew up Beaumont Hill and turned left at the garage."

The pilot needs to know the direction and strength of the upper wind. The wind at 16,000 feet or 33,000 feet is not the same as at the surface. In simple language, if he is flying to Southampton with a westerly wind, he may have to point the aircraft to Weymouth. In the old days they just pointed it towards England and hoped for the best. Incredibly, there was a remarkable level of safety even if the passengers never learned what the pilot was going through. Pilots such as Captain Caldwell were flying to Southampton from the first days, as was Captain Keene-Miller. An old lady making her first flight saw land through the cloud asked anxiously, "Do you think the driver knows where we are?"

Before closing, it must be said that the Channel Islands 'made Weymouth.' People who would have never visited it saw the splendid beach and the pleasant places around such as Lulworth Cove. The increasing number of ships, some with more than a thousand passengers, caused the Council and the Railway Company to extend the railway from Weymouth Station to Weymouth Pier. This involved the lines being laid in a main street, and it was necessary for a man with a red flag to precede the train. The curves were so severe that there had to be three links between the carriages, and thus a big gap. Portable steps were brought to the carriage doors where the station was too short.

But it was not only the passengers who came and went. The goods trade with Jersey potatoes, tomatoes and cauliflowers, plus Guernsey tomatoes, brought employment and many more trains and passengers vehicles. At times there were two or three passenger trains of full length and three goods trains on the pier at the same time. The passenger trains had the distinction of being Boat Trains and carried a restaurant car.

When all this came to an end and things moved to Poole, Weymouth slumped; Condor came back but not the goods. The Common Market with its lorries, and lorries with their containers from Jersey has had a marked effect on the railway. The lines from the quay have gone, and so has the thrilling ride through the streets.

Richard Mayne, in his book *Mail Ships from the Channel Islands* quotes 99 ships by name. Although some sank and were refloated, the following were wrecked and went to a watery grave instead of the breakers' yard:

Name	Built	Rig	Remarks
Francis Feeling	1811	Cutter	Wrecked in 1826
Hinchinbrook	1811	Cutter	Wrecked in 1826
Meteor	1821	Wooden paddle steamer	Wrecked in 1830
Express	1847	Iron paddle steamer	Wrecked in 1859
Brighton	1856	Iron paddle steamer	Wrecked in 1887
Normandy 1	1863	Iron paddle steamer	Wrecked in 1870
Caesarea 1	1867	Iron screw steamer	Wrecked in 1884
Waverley	1865	Iron paddle steamer	Wrecked in 1873
Guernsey	1874	Iron screw steamer	Wrecked in 1815
South Western 2	1874	Iron screw steamer	Torpedoed 1915
Diana	1876	Iron screw steamer	Wrecked in 1895
Caledonia	1876	Iron screw steamer	Wrecked in 1881
Hilda	1882	Iron screw steamer	Wrecked in 1905
Laura	1885	Steel screw steamer	Wrecked in Bahamas
Stella	1890	Steel twin-screw steamer	Wrecked in 1899
Roebuck	1897	Twin screw steamer	Sank in 1915 whilst R.N.
Princess Ena	1906	Twin screw turbine	Caught fire and sank 1935
Sarnia 1	1910	Triple screw turbine	Torpedoed in 1918
Normannia	1910	Twin screw turbine	Lost at Dunkirk 1940
Lorina	1918	Twin screw turbine	Lost at Dunkirk 1940
St. Brieuc	1924	Twin screw turbine	Lost in 1942
St. Patrick	1930	Twin screw turbine	Bombed and lost in 1941

The Occupation showed what happens when there are no ships and no aircraft. People starved and there were no imports or exports. The tale of the mailboats and cargo ships is one of stunning courage and heroism against all the odds of weather and tides. But is has always been taken for granted.

Ships travel along the English Channel from west to east or east to west. Our ships travel from south to north and north to south. It is the equivalent of crossing the M1.

The heroism in the war was of the highest order, but has seldom been acknowledged or recorded. We were glad to see the ships back, but many were bombed and sunk.

What is really interesting is that, apart from the war, no ship has been wrecked since the 1930s if we don't count the *Princess Ena* which caught fire and sank in 1935. The coming of radio, radar, navigation aids and lighthouses has transformed the situation. We must add to that the construction of ships with watertight compartments. Travel by sea is as safe as travel by air or travel by train.

Things now are all on a huge scale. There were 600 letters per day to deliver in 1750. In 1994 the Jersey Post Office handled 3,250,000. The cost of the early ships was a few thousand pounds. Today the fast ships of 35 knots costs in the region of £20 million.

AND NOW – FAREWELL

Farewell! a word that hath been and must be;
A sound that makes us linger — yet farewell!

The weather in Jersey is very moderate. When we rejoice over various conditions and wonder if the climate is changing, the figures we record are trivial compared with most other places in the world. We should rejoice that the Island is as nearly perfect as it is possible to be. If we cannot find happiness here, it is difficult to think of an alternative which is better. Hardly anyone is killed by storm, tempest, floods, lightning, heat or cold. There are no severe earthquakes or devastating volcanoes. Storms at sea cause occasional loss of life, but major tragedies are almost unknown.

It is not always realised what a large area of the earth's surface is under snow and ice, and therefore almost uninhabitable — namely the Arctic and Antarctic. Then there are huge areas of land which are too hot and dry to sustain much life — the Sahara Desert in Africa and the Gobi Desert in China to name but two. If we write off Siberia as being almost hopeless, we find that the amount of land rendered uninhabitable by weather conditions is almost as great as the earth's surface which sustains human life in comfort.

Man cannot destroy what has been created because matter is indestructible. When we rightly deplore the destruction of rain forests, we must remember that trees grow again, so we cannot lose them permanently. If everyone left Britain, the country would become the jungle it once was, and people poking around a thousand years hence would find the remains of a city called London.

There have been claims down the years that the world is running out of coal — it isn't — but even if it was, coal would continue to form under the earth. It is the same with oil. If we use up the amount we have found so far we would have to do without it for a few centuries, but it would continue to be generated. The earth cannot cease to be without coal, oil, water and so forth.

When we marvel that there are those who can climb Mount Everest, 29,002 feet on the borders of Nepal and Tibet in the Himalayas, not many realise that the deepest sea is more than 29,000 feet down, and nobody can ever see the life-forms in that unknown part of the world. The tides are not governed by us, nor can we alter them. They are governed by the moon which is, on average, 239,000 miles away.

The seasons are an essential part of life. The first scent of spring brings new life to the earth. Then the heat of Lady Summer who gives us twice the amount of daylight that Old Man Winter allows. The Fall — autumn — with the colours, the harvest and the sadness of falling dying leaves. Finally the death of so much in winter with its barreness, but with the sure knowledge of the resurrection, new life and the rising of the sap in the trees. It is the contrast that is exciting. Would we really want the garden to be full of spring flowers permanently, and would we want each day to be brilliantly sunny throughout the year?

We have been given dominion over all the earth, and therefore we can live and survive in any part of the globe. But there is barely another creature or plant that can do so in the wild. Elephants cannot live where polar bears live; fish can live within limits of sea temperature suitable for them; deep-sea fish cannot live in shallows; rain forests are not seen at the Poles because cold air cannot hold the moisture that warm air can to give the necessary rain. Each form of life has its own habitation which is governed and controlled by the weather and climate.

If we take great empires which have waxed and waned down the ages – the Roman Empire; British Empire; Persian Empire; Spanish Empire and so forth – we find that no great nation has ever arisen within the tropics, nor within the Arctic or Antarctic zones. That is a very large part of the earth's surface, and it is entirely due to climate. Only mad dogs and Englishmen toil in the mid-day sun.

It is said that the greatest numbers of people who live to over 100 – and even to 130 years – is in Siberia. These people often have no access to doctors, no hypermarkets, and only basic food, but they survive in atrocious conditions. On the other hand we chastise the government in very cold weather and claim that old people suffer from hypothermia when all they need do is put on more clothes. When we run out of oil at a week-end in winter, we feel that we are bound to catch a cold.

The truth is that we are made to survive anywhere naturally. But our aim in life – our standard of living – insists that we should get through life as comfortably and painlessly as possible. Hence central heating in winter and fans and cooling air in summer so that we generate our own climates in the home and in the car, and don't have to walk too much in the open. We should watch the pageantry in the sky with the ever-changing patterns of clouds, and try to read the signs which tell us what is to come.

The author hopes that those who turn to the weather and tides in the future will find the same thrill and excitement that he found. This is because the power of nature is enormous. A single intense depression in mid-Atlantic generates far more energy than can be generated by the most powerful atomic bomb, and the fury of earthquakes and volcanoes is beyond the comprehension of mankind.

The author acknowledges that he was never the master; the weather was the master of him, but it has been a challenge and it has given him happiness and spiritual enlightenment for virtually the whole of his life.

As we move towards retirement
These in the main are our regrets.
That when we're right no one remembers
But when we're wrong no one forgets.

Lightning behind Elizabeth Castle on 28 August 1931. It was the wettest day and the most severe thunderstorm this century.